Praise for

"*Doctor in the House…*
The dialogue, the characters, the scenes never hit a false note."
—*Romantic Times BOOKreviews*

"Marie Ferrarella's *Romancing the Teacher* has a nicely constructed plot, abundant warmth and humor, plus great characters—especially the hero."
—*Romantic Times BOOKreviews*

"Marie Ferrarella does a great job of blending humor with intrigue."
—*Romantic Times BOOKreviews* on *Diagnosis: Danger*

"*Finding Home* is wonderful, filled with humor and heart. The picture of a husband who means well but hasn't a clue is dead-on."
—*Romantic Times BOOKreviews*

Marie Ferrarella

by Marie Ferrarella is perfect

SAFE HAVEN

MARIE FERRARELLA

Caitlin's Guardian Angel

Silhouette Books

Published by Silhouette Books

America's Publisher of Contemporary Romance

If you purchased this book without a cover you should be aware
that this book is stolen property. It was reported as "unsold and
destroyed" to the publisher, and neither the author nor the
publisher has received any payment for this "stripped book."

SILHOUETTE BOOKS

ISBN-13: 978-0-373-36156-4
ISBN-10:   0-373-36156-4

CAITLIN'S GUARDIAN ANGEL

Copyright © 1995 by Marie Rydzynski-Ferrarella

All rights reserved. Except for use in any review, the reproduction
or utilization of this work in whole or in part in any form by any
electronic, mechanical or other means, now known or hereafter
invented, including xerography, photocopying and recording, or in
any information storage or retrieval system, is forbidden without
the written permission of the editorial office, Silhouette Books,
233 Broadway, New York, NY 10279 U.S.A.

This is a work of fiction. Names, characters, places and incidents are
either the product of the author's imagination or are used fictitiously,
and any resemblance to actual persons, living or dead, business establishments,
events or locales is entirely coincidental.

This edition published by arrangement with Harlequin Books S.A.

® and TM are trademarks of Harlequin Books S.A., used under license.
Trademarks indicated with ® are registered in the United States Patent
and Trademark Office, the Canadian Trade Marks Office and in other
countries.

Visit Silhouette Books at www.eHarlequin.com

Printed in U.S.A.

MARIE FERRARELLA

This *USA TODAY* bestselling and RITA® Award-winning author has written more than 180 books for Silhouette Books, some under the name Marie Nicole. Her romances are beloved by fans worldwide.

To Leslie Wainger,
who turned out to be a guardian angel
in her own right: mine.
Thank you, Leslie, for everything.

Prologue

She was late.

A hint of the sizzling heat to come wafted to her as she hurried across the sidewalk to the alley.

There were very few things that Caitlin Cassidy hated as much as being late. This morning it seemed as if the forces of God and nature had conspired to see just how far they could push her. Her alarm had failed to go off. She'd woken up with a start to a neighbor's barking dog, twenty minutes behind schedule before she ever set foot on the floor. The tone for the day had been sent.

When she'd slipped behind the wheel, the starter motor on her car had sputtered and sounded on the brink of death before kicking over. She'd held her breath as she'd driven through the sleeping streets of Phoenix, willing the vehicle not to die before she reached her shop. She'd just barely made it, she thought as she hurried now through the winding alley.

Caitlin took a deep breath of the warm, early-morning air. *Enjoy it while it lasts.* The city would heat up quickly. Phoenix's spring was everyone else's summer.

Directly overhead, the dawn sky was filled with long, thin

fingers of intense purple, grasping to pull away the final curtain of night. It was going to be a hot one, she mused. Bad
for business. Fewer customers window-shopping.

The heels of her beige shoes echoed in the narrow alleyway. An alleyway she wouldn't have had to take if the city
hadn't whimsically decided to repave the parking area directly
before her store and the accompanying lot. The entire area
had been partitioned off for a week now and she'd had to
park her car three long blocks away.

The alley, networking behind two strip malls that stood
back-to-back like two duelists, was a shortcut to her store.
She didn't like coming this way, but she had wanted to get
an early start this morning.

She wasn't late by anyone's standards but her own. As the
owner of a small, exclusive lingerie shop, she could have
come waltzing in at noon if she chose. What she chose was
to be there a full two hours before she switched the gaily
printed cardboard sign from Closed to Open. There was always something to do. Accounts to go over, like this morning,
merchandise to rearrange or simply the opportunity to stand
back and silently absorb the fact that Naughty But Nice was
hers.

The sound of raised voices cut through her musings like a
hot knife slicing through a chilled pie. Angry voices, buzzing
like bees swarming around a hive that had been invaded. The
words were coming so quickly, it was hard for her to distin-
guish what was being said, only how it was being said.

Anger reeked in the alleyway like three-day-old garbage
left out in the sun, turning her stomach.

Warning her.

Instinctively Caitlin moved to accept the shelter of a grimy,
discolored brick building. Sidestepping a Dumpster, Caitlin
inched her way forward to the sound of the voices.

As she approached, she realized that only one of the voices
was angry; the other—high, reedy—belonged to someone
who was genuinely frightened.

Caitlin held her breath as she peered around the corner of
the building. Up ahead, squared off in diminishing shadows,

were two men. The angry man, taller than the other, far better dressed, stood with his back to her.

"Thought I wouldn't catch on, didn't you, little man?"

The man he addressed shook visibly. He was as thin as his voice. "No, I swear, no. I didn't mean no harm. It was just this once, honest."

"Honest?" The taller man's voice, more polished than his companion's, dropped to a low, deadly purr as he turned the word around on his tongue. "Strange word for a man who's been cheating his employer."

Fear melded with the stench of anger. Caitlin could almost smell it where she stood. Her heart raced in her chest.

"It won't happen again. I swear on my mother's grave it won't happen again. It's just that I got these debts, see, and these guys are really mean."

"Meaner than I?"

The low laugh that accompanied the question froze Caitlin's heart.

Eagerness punctuated the smaller man's jerky movements. "Oh, yes, yes."

"I sincerely doubt that."

"Oh, no, they're a lot meaner." His squeaky voice cracked.

It happened so quickly Caitlin didn't absorb it at first.

There was a glint of metallic gray as the well-dressed man pulled something from his jacket. In its wake came a slight *pop*. Horror streaked across the thin man's face, freezing there as he dropped to his knees. He fell, a puppet whose strings had been severed. Blood bubbled relentlessly from the hole in his chest.

"You...you...shot...me." They were the last words the thin man was to utter.

His executioner looked down at him as if he enjoyed the sight of life draining away from a man like water running through a sieve. "As I said, I sincerely doubt that they're meaner than I. I guess you won't be cheating anyone anymore, eh, little man?"

The laugh was low, guttural and not quite sane.

Stunned, dazed, horrified, Caitlin drew in her breath. She

saw the gunman's head jerk up and turn in her direction, listening, like a wolf who'd scented the approach of an enemy.

Caitlin pulled back from the opening, wishing herself invisible. By the time she'd reached the open street, she was running.

Only one question throbbed in her brain.

Had he seen her?

Chapter 1

"Look alive, Gray, the captain wants to see us in his office ASAP."

Detective Graham Redhawk sighed. He had been in the office exactly three minutes, not even long enough to pour himself a cup of what Sergeant Terrance Farantino brewed every morning and laughingly referred to as coffee.

Eyes the color of the liquid he was contemplating glanced up to study the man who spoke. Rather than drop everything to follow him, Graham measured out a full mug, then set the stained, dingy glass pot back on the warmer. Because there were times on the job that required lightning speed, Graham took the rest of life at a reduced pace. Life always had a habit of catching up with you whether or not you hurried toward it.

"Can't it wait until I drink this sludge?" He indicated the mug with his eyes. "It doesn't feel as if I've started my day unless I feel Farantino's coffee oozing through my veins."

Ben Jeffers had no idea how Redhawk could bear to drink that stuff. But then, in the past seven years that they'd been partnered, Jeffers had learned that there were a great many pieces to Redhawk's puzzle that he would never figure out. He wasn't the easiest man to understand, but he made a hell of a partner.

Jeffers nodded toward the beige mug Graham held in his hands. "Bring it with you." He was already edging his way toward the rear of the room. "Captain's frowning and it's not a pretty sight."

Graham took a healthy swallow before commenting. "The captain," he corrected, "is not a pretty sight."

Jeffers laughed. Captain Asa Martinez was a straight arrow who needed to be reminded from time to time what it meant to be human. Few had enough nerve to remind him. Redhawk, it was clear from early on, was never short of nerve. "Don't I know it."

The two men walked through the large fishbowl that was otherwise known as the detectives' room, weaving through too many people, desks and chairs as they worked their way toward the rear. Graham could see Martinez from his vantage point in the room.

Captain Martinez sat in his small, glass-enclosed office at the back of the squad room. Fluorescent light gleamed off the sheen on his bald head that was damp with perspiration. The air-conditioning was behaving like an asthmatic unit suffering an attack, huffing cool air out sporadically at will.

Martinez did not have the appearance of a happy man.

Graham had seen that look before. Something was up. "If those lines on his face get any deeper, you could lose cars in them."

Jeffers thought of the '59 pink Cadillac Eldorado that Redhawk drove. It was his pride and joy, despite the razzing he received from the men. He treated it the way a man did his mistress.

"Not your car." Jeffers stole a piece of peppermint candy out of an openmouthed jar Detective Chambers kept on his desk. According to the sign-out board, Chambers was on stakeout. Jeffers popped the candy into his mouth as he walked by. "Take a damn chasm before that car'd disappear."

Graham sidestepped an officer ushering a scantily clad young woman off to be fingerprinted. She looked no older than seventeen and as yet was missing that jaded, worn look that was so often the stamp of a hooker. He wondered if she had anyone who cared enough to save her.

"I don't like driving my Caddy in rough terrain," he told Jeffers.

He stopped before the captain's door and took another long swallow of his coffee. Graham took a deep breath as the hot brew inched its way through his veins, systematically waking up everything in its path and bringing it to attention. Not that he wasn't alert without it, but it helped.

Graham opened the door and let Jeffers walk in first. Slipping in, he closed the door quietly behind him.

"You wanted to see us, Captain?" He leaned a shoulder indolently against the doorjamb, still nursing his coffee. There were two extra chairs in the small room, but he remained where he was. Graham preferred standing to sitting. It took less time to spring into action that way.

Jeffers took a seat closer to the wall.

Martinez threw down the report he was wading through and rubbed his face with his hands. It had been eighteen months since he'd had a real vacation and he was about twenty-four months overdue. It never got easier.

"Took your sweet time getting your tails in here," Martinez observed gruffly. The commissioner was leaning on him and that never improved his mood. "As of seven this morning, we have ourselves another homicide. Victim went down between Sunflower and Alameda. No ID on him. Two sets of track marks on his arms."

"What a surprise," Graham commented into his mug, tilting it as he drained the remainder. "And it was such a nice morning, too."

Martinez was accustomed to Redhawk's sarcasm. The man was a maverick who fitted in only when he chose to. When push came to shove, Martinez knew he'd rather have a squad of Redhawks backing him up in a dangerous situation than a building full of by-the-book detectives.

Martinez thought of the long, drawn-out meeting with the commissioner the previous afternoon. The unsolved cases were escalating. "Might get nicer if we figured out who did it."

Graham had long ago given up the itch to solve each puzzle, close each case. Some stayed with him longer than others and his record was better than most, but he didn't wear blinders when it came to reality. Life had ripped the blinders from him at a very young age. He knew most cases went unsolved.

"Odds, Captain?"

Trust Redhawk to point out the downside, Martinez thought, keeping his impatience in check. "Are against us, usually," he agreed. He tapped a copy of the call that had come into 911 earlier. "But this time we've got a witness."

Graham arched a brow as he exchanged looks with Jeffers. He'd written down too many statements from eyewitnesses who swore the same man was five foot nothing and six-three to get excited.

"Reliable?"

Martinez glanced at the information the dispatcher had taken down upon routine questioning. "Young, Caucasian female, shopkeeper, well-to-do family. No criminal record—not even a parking ticket. No glasses or contacts." Deep-set, mud brown eyes swept over the two men in his office. "I'd say probably as reliable as we're lucky enough to get." At least he could hope. Twenty-two years on the job and he could still hope. He thought that might be some kind of record. "I want you to go and take down her statement."

Jeffers groaned.

Martinez directed a steely gaze in his direction. "You've got a problem with that?"

That it was futile to protest was a foregone conclusion, but Jeffers gave it a try. He'd always been the vocal one of the team. "Captain, our caseload is bursting at the seams."

Martinez slapped a wide palm against his equally wide chest. "Hear that?" After a beat, Jeffers shook his head. "No? Then let me tell you what it is. That's the sound of my heart *not* breaking.'' Martinez dropped his hand heavily to his desk. ''Nobody told you this life was going to be easy.''

Jeffers rose to his feet. His grin was slow and easy. ''I dunno. In the movies they always solve things in two hours.''

Martinez shook his head. He'd give up half his pension to make that a reality. It'd be nice to have a stack of solved cases instead of unsolved ones. ''Then go to the movies.'' He jerked a thumb at the door. ''On your way out, leave your badge at the desk.''

Jeffers laughed shortly. It was Martinez's way of telling him to quit dreaming and get to work. ''You drive a hard bargain, Captain.''

Graham allowed himself a small smile for his partner's benefit. ''That's what makes him captain.'' His eyes shifted toward his superior. He appreciated the fact that Martinez cut him slack now and again. Though they were as far from alike as two men could be, they respected each other. It was as good as it got. Redhawk knew how to get far on very little. ''This reliable witness, does she have a name?''

Martinez pushed forward his report and placed the information on the corner of his desk for the detective's benefit. ''They usually do. She called in about an hour ago.'' He tapped a piece of paper. The name and address were written on it. ''We've already got men on the scene of the crime.''

Graham covered the paper with his hand, his eyes still on the captain. ''Where's the witness now?''

''In her shop.'' Martinez leaned back in his chair, and it squeaked in protest. ''She called from there. Dispatch told her to stay put, that someone would be by to take her statement.'' His eyes met Graham's. ''You'd be that someone. You can borrow a uniform from the site of the investigation if you want.''

Graham shook his head. There was no reason to take extra men on a routine questioning. ''No, Jeffers'll do.''

''Thanks,'' his partner said dryly.

Graham squinted at the paper. The address was clear enough, but the witness's name was a mass of scribbles. ''I can't make out the name." He looked up at Martinez. "Hell, Captain, you guys should brush up on your penmanship."

"Just as soon as you brush up on your manners." Martinez leaned forward and took the paper back. He paused a moment, remembering more than reading. "Catherine. No, Caitlin. Caitlin Cassidy."

He handed the paper back to Redhawk. If he hadn't known any better, he would have said that the detective had paled. His jaw was definitely clenched. "Know her?"

"Yeah." There wasn't one shred of emotion in his voice as Graham shoved the paper into the pocket of his jeans. "I know her."

"You're a hell of a lot braver than I am, Cait," Kerry Sawyer told her best friend as she ran long, spidery fingers up and down her arms nervously. Ever since Caitlin had told her about the early-morning shooting that had taken place only blocks from the shop, she'd felt a numbing chill in the air. It was something she'd thought was in her past. "If I had seen somebody shooting somebody else, I would've gotten out of there as quick as I could and forgotten I ever saw anything." Non-involvement had been the rule of thumb that had guided her childhood.

Caitlin stared at the petite blonde. They had shared a dorm room together. More than that, they had shared hopes and dreams. It had been Kerry who had first seen this shop up for sale and had urged her to make the commitment. After eight years, Caitlin thought she knew Kerry inside and out. She couldn't believe that Kerry was actually suggesting that she turn her back on a moral obligation.

"I couldn't do that."

Clearly worried, Kerry shook her head. "My mama always said don't go borrowing trouble, and this is trouble with a capital *T*."

Caitlin moved restlessly around the back room. In front, their part-time salesgirl, Eva, was helping customers. The shop seemed like a million miles away. Caitlin blew out a breath, wondering when her adrenaline was going to settle down again. "I wasn't borrowing it—it was thrown at me."

Kerry's wide mouth turned down in a deep frown. Sometimes Caitlin was a little too noble. She still didn't understand things about the underbelly of life. Kerry had grown up in a neighborhood where death stalked the streets daily, as much a reality as morning coffee. Sometimes more. Kerry's protective nature emerged in full bloom. "You didn't have to catch it."

It wasn't in Caitlin to ignore the unignorable. "Kerry, if everyone pretended not to see, this would be a very scary world."

Kerry placed a hand on Caitlin's shoulder. "Not if everyone minded their own business." Caitlin was older by eight months, but in so many ways she was an innocent. It was part of the reason they were friends.

The agitation Caitlin was feeling spilled out in her voice. "I can't believe you. Do you actually mean to tell me that if you saw someone shot, you wouldn't report it?"

It was more of a dilemma than Caitlin knew. Kerry sighed. "I know the difference between right and wrong, Cait, but that's for the other guy." Kerry waved a hand vaguely. "For television shows where they still wear white hats and black hats and things get resolved tidily." She took hold of her friend's shoulders. She didn't want to think of anything happening to Caitlin. "What if you identify this creep and he finds out about it? What if he comes looking for you to eliminate the witness?"

Caitlin blew out a long breath. "Thanks, Kerry, I needed that."

Kerry threw up her hands, knowing it was useless to argue. Caitlin put a fine spin on stubbornness. "I just don't want you taking any unnecessary chances, Cait, that's all."

Caitlin's annoyance softened. She realized that it was just nerves that were making her so defensive. "Thanks for worrying, but I have to be able to look at myself in the mirror, too."

"At least you'd be alive to look."

This was nonsense, Caitlin thought, hiding out in the back room, waiting for her nerves to cease short-circuiting. She'd feel a lot better mingling with her customers. No matter what, she always felt better around people. Her mother had accused her more than once of being far too friendly.

Caitlin smiled to herself, wondering what her mother would have to say about this. She hoped that it wouldn't reach the newspapers. One of her mother's friends was bound to see and call her about it. God knew *she* wasn't about to call her mother and volunteer the story. These days she and her mother spoke at an absolute minimum. When Caitlin did call, it was out of a sense of duty. The need for approval had long since passed, and in any event, Caitlin knew that nothing she did would ever please Regina Langford Cassidy or reflect well, in her mother's estimation, on the lineage that was so very precious to her.

"I'm going out to do some work," Caitlin announced to Kerry.

Caitlin glanced at herself in the small mirror that hung on the wall near the door. Her mouth was pale. She'd bitten off her lipstick. That had probably happened during the 911 call she'd placed. The one with her heart lodged in her throat. She'd been so agitated, Caitlin was surprised that she had gotten any words out at all.

"Here," Kerry said, handing her a tube of lipstick. "We don't want you frightening away the customers." She offered Caitlin an encouraging smile. Stubborn or not, she was still her best friend.

By the time Kerry had arrived in the shop, Caitlin had had an hour to calm herself down. She was no longer shaking. At least, not outwardly.

Inwardly was a different story. With no effort at all, Caitlin could still see the look of horror on the little man's face as he dropped to the pavement. She could still see the blood flowing from him like an angry red river, pooling along his body.

And she probably would for a very long time to come.

Struggling against being engulfed by the memory, she

twisted the top off the lipstick and reapplied the slight sheen of pink to her lips. Unconsciously squaring her shoulders, Caitlin walked out of the back room.

The shop was long and narrow and had an elegance to it that she was proud of. She'd taken great pains to decorate it so that it reflected exactly what she had pictured in her mind—old-world class. Cutting corners, she and Kerry had hung the patterned wallpaper themselves.

"Like common people," her mother had chastised angrily. Regina Cassidy hadn't wanted Caitlin to buy the shop in the first place, especially not if she was going to actually work in it. Her mother was of the opinion that when you were born into wealth, you had an obligation to your forebears to perpetuate an aura. That meant socializing with the right people, doing and saying the right things.

In the beginning, Caitlin had attempted to abide by her mother's rules. She had been the obedient daughter until she reached high school. At fifteen she had struck her first blow for independence by insisting on going to the local public high school instead of boarding at one of the private schools her mother thought worthy of a Cassidy. Her father, bless him, had backed her up, and she had gotten her way.

And her life had irrevocably changed when she'd stepped through the front doors of Horace Greeley High.

With effort, Caitlin blanked out her mind. She didn't want to think about that now, didn't want to think about anything except the handful of women who were in the store, drifting from display to display.

She chose one and focused on her. Putting on her best smile, Caitlin approached the slightly bemused older woman. "Hello, may I help you with something?"

The woman held a teddy in her hands. It was almost as red as the blush on her cheeks. She looked at Caitlin a little uncertainly. Caitlin recognized embarrassment when she saw it.

The woman shrugged helplessly as she fiddled with the teddy's satin straps. "My James said that I should buy myself something slinky for our anniversary. Married to the man for thirty years and now he wants slinky."

Caitlin laughed. It was a soft, mellow sound that drifted in the scented air between them and set the woman instantly at ease. Behind her, the tiny bell at the door announced the entrance of another customer. Caitlin had opted for an old-fashioned bell rather than any other intrusive sound, such as a buzzer. She supposed she was an old-fashioned girl at heart, a throwback to another, more romantic era.

She smiled at the woman. "Lucky for you you have the figure for it."

The woman visibly bloomed. The glow of embarrassment on her cheeks turned to one of anticipation and excitement at the possibility of an adventure. She regarded the teddy with new interest.

"Is there somewhere I can...?" Her voice trailed off.

"The dressing rooms are on the right." Caitlin pointed toward the three discreetly curtained booths in the rear. She saw Kerry emerging from the office. "Kerry will take care of you," she promised as the latter came forward. "Selecting the right one isn't always easy." She handed the teddy to Kerry and ushered the customer toward the dressing area. "Take all the time you need to decide. Kerry will assist you if you need something else."

"First time?" Kerry asked. When the woman nodded, Kerry glanced at the teddy in her hand. "Great choice."

Kerry, Caitlin thought, was one of those people who could sell ice to Inuits.

She turned toward the door, ready to assist the next customer. For the second time that morning, Caitlin froze. The first time horror had stiffened her limbs. This time it was disbelief.

She felt as if she had been plucked up and bodily deposited into the past.

He'd felt it, Graham realized, as soon as he'd entered the store and heard her laugh. That old feeling had washed over him, as sure, as strong as if it were a physical wave. That old feeling that had always wrenched his gut and reduced him from a six-foot-two strapping man into someone whom he hardly recognized.

Or was willing to admit to.

He felt it even though it had been years since he had seen her. Years since she had been part of his life. And torn it into shreds.

There were times, even now, when he'd be reminded of her. A song, a word; a stray, unbidden thought and she would drift back to him like some sort of unattainable dream he would never be free of. Some sort of spell he couldn't break.

But that was his problem. And problems were something he never let interfere with his work. If he did, he wouldn't have been able to remain on the police force for as long as he had. He would have been a walking liability, to himself and his partner. Being a cop, a good cop, was all he had ever wanted to be.

She was still standing, Caitlin realized. Her legs hadn't dissolved under her. Funny how the hurt could spring up so fast, so fierce after all this time. What had it been? Ten? No, eleven years. Eleven long years. Long enough for feelings to fade.

Most feelings.

There wasn't enough time in the world, she thought, to completely separate her from the anguish that had once claimed her. But with time, she had managed to successfully numb it and function.

Struggling to strip all emotion from her voice, Caitlin turned icy blue eyes toward Graham. She scarcely noticed the shorter, sandy-haired man with him. But then, Graham had a way of filling up spaces the way no other man could.

"May I help you?"

There wasn't an ounce of feeling in her voice. But what had he expected? She'd evaporated out of his life as if she'd never existed. He had gone to her house looking for her when at the last minute she had abruptly changed plans for their elopement. He'd gone looking, hoping she could be convinced to change her mind again. Praying she would. Knowing he had no right to ask her to start a life with him, thinking he would die inside if she wouldn't marry him.

She hadn't.

And he hadn't died.

What doesn't kill you makes you stronger, he thought. It was one of those trite sayings that rang true. He had had a wealth of Native American sayings passed on to him, guiding his steps as a child. He'd had precious little else.

Graham nodded at her, stiff, polite, as if he'd never sampled the warmth of her mouth. "Caitlin."

The years had been kind to him, etching their stamp upon his face and giving him a rugged warrior appearance. Given his heritage, it was appropriate. What was he doing here after all this time?

Her voice was as formal, as stiff as his. "Graham."

There was enough frost in here to make a man go rummaging for his overcoat, Jeffers thought. He looked from his partner to the attactive woman. They looked like two boxers, entering the ring just before the bell sounded. Whatever had gone down between them must have been big.

Taking the lead, Jeffers fished his wallet out of his jacket. He flipped it open to his shield and raised it toward Caitlin. He had to hold it up to get her attention. "Ms. Cassidy, we're with the Phoenix P.D. I'm Detective Jeffers and I gather you already know Detective Redhawk."

A police detective? Her eyes shifted toward Graham in surprise. She remembered that he'd talked about entering law enforcement, but she'd thought him too much of a rebel to work within the system. He'd never been one to take orders.

This was all she needed, to be haunted by a ghost from her past. Caitlin pressed her lips together and nodded in response to Jeffers's question.

"Yes, I do."

Definitely something big, Jeffers thought as he noted the look of animosity that ricocheted between his partner and the woman. Unless he missed his guess, it was going to be a hell of a challenge not to get caught in the cross fire.

"You placed a call to 911 earlier this morning," Jeffers prodded gently when the other two remained silent. "About a murder."

The last word roused her and brought back the cold chill she'd felt. Caitlin was, if nothing else, a survivor. She had a reputation to maintain as well as an aura to perpetuate for the sake of her business. The last thing she wanted was to have that image sullied by talk of murders and men bleeding to death in alleys.

With an air of studied nonchalance, Caitlin casually looked around the store to see if anyone had overheard. But other than glancing curiously at the two men, who looked as out of place amid the lingerie as two hockey players in a ballet, the other customers seemed oblivious to what was transpiring.

At least he hadn't managed to ruin this for her, as well. Biting the corner of her lip, Caitlin turned toward the rear.

"If you two gentlemen will follow me to the back office, I think we can talk more easily there."

He doubted that, Graham thought as he fell into step behind Jeffers. Doubted that he could speak more easily anywhere Caitlin was. The way she'd nibbled on her lower lip had brought another salvo of memories back to him.

It was as if all those years hadn't happened. As if he was still just that self-conscious kid fresh off the reservation, trying to find his way in a world he thought hostile toward him.

Almost unwillingly, his eyes skimmed over Caitlin as she led the way to the rear of the store. Her silhouette had gotten shapelier. Riper. And her golden brown hair had gotten longer. It fell over her shoulders like a honeyed waterfall.

Graham tried not to remember how he used to like running his fingers through it. How much he had enjoyed burying his face in it and inhaling its scent. The scent always reminded him of a field of wildflowers. Like the field where he had once almost taken her, until restraint and common sense had stepped in the way and prevented him.

She'd been so young, so innocent. He'd wanted to save it until their wedding night. Cynicism curved his mouth. He'd turned out to be the one who was young and innocent.

And a fool.

There were years between then and now. And a wall separating them, a wall he'd once been stupid enough to believe could be surmounted.

He knew better now, and he had her to thank for teaching him.

Chapter 2

The atmosphere within the back room was oppressive. It hung heavy with the smell of dust and cardboard. In actuality, the room was little more than an appendage that had been added on as an afterthought. It had been carved out of the main showroom to give Caitlin somewhere to go when she needed a break.

Determined to maintain some degree of privacy, Caitlin tugged on the curtain to shut them away from the customers. The loops snagged and remained in place, refusing to move along the rod. She pulled again, stretching up on her toes for leverage and accidentally brushing against Graham's shoulder.

Ignoring the whisper of warmth that flashed through him, Graham nudged her silently aside. Grasping the material in his hand, he snapped his wrist. The loops slid along as easily as if the rod had been greased with oil.

Graham released the curtain and backed as far away as he could within the room's minuscule dimensions. The space became even smaller.

The room was filled with neatly stacked, colorful catalogs

that had yet to be shipped out. Pressed directly against the opposite wall was a desk hardly large enough to accommodate the computer standing on it, yet too large for the available space.

A sneeze would have caused the room to explode, Jeffers mused. It was definitely not a place for three people to stand and talk. Especially if two of those people didn't want to be within several light-years of each other.

Jeffers casually glanced from one face to the other. Both seemed ridged with tension. He wondered what had gone down between the two and how long it would be before something erupted.

That an eruption was coming he had no doubt. For the present, it was like standing on the edge of a volcano, feeling the rumbling going on just beneath his feet.

Her scent was everywhere, Graham thought. It came like the creeping early-morning mist, surrounding him. Though it was lighter than spring, it sealed him in. He'd been aware of it in the main room of the store. Here, inside this tiny alcove, it was overwhelming.

For a moment he thought of leaving, of letting Jeffers handle the case. The man was more than capable of taking down whatever statement she had to give. He didn't need this now. Or at all.

But Martinez had placed him in charge. Leaving it to Jeffers would mean shirking his duties for personal reasons and that was completely unacceptable to him. Nothing got in the way of his being a cop. Ever. It, along with Jake and pride in his heritage, made him what he was. *Who* he was. To step away because he had once thought himself in love with her was cowardice.

And cowards never slept peacefully. Graham liked his sleep.

Very carefully he edged Jeffers aside and placed himself next to Caitlin. Next to the woman he once would have died for. Next to the woman who had killed the part of him that had yearned to be like everyone else.

Maybe he should be grateful to her, he thought. She had

shown him once and for all that he wasn't like everyone else. Half-white, half-Navajo, he belonged only in the world that he'd created for himself.

Graham looked at her in silence for a long moment. "What happened?"

Caitlin raised her head to look into his eyes. If he thought she was going to look away, he would be disappointed. She wasn't the starry-eyed girl she'd once been. He'd seen to that.

Nonetheless, his question erased the years. For just a fragment of a moment, she wasn't standing here on the outer edge of a decade and more; she was a girl just out of high school, wondering the same question as she looked down at the token he had given her. A token of his heritage. *What happened?*

A token of his love. Or so she had foolishly believed.

Her words felt as if they'd traveled a great distance before reaching her lips. "You tell me," she whispered, her eyes angry, demanding.

The silence and animosity in the air was thick enough to cut with a knife. Jeffers cleared his throat. After a beat, both sets of eyes turned toward him.

"You made a 911 call," he prompted easily.

His gentle, coaxing voice brought Caitlin back across the years and to this morning. Taking a shaky breath, she nodded. "Yes. Yes, I did."

Caitlin fastened her eyes on the shorter man. Things would go a lot more smoothly for her if she just concentrated on him and not Graham. Graham didn't concern her anymore. He'd ceased to be a great many years ago. What there had been between them was dead. He had killed it. She had got over that and gone on with her life. A life she was very proud of.

Without thinking, she placed her hand on top of one of the catalogs. It grounded her.

This was reality. Her business, the murder she had witnessed this morning, here and now. Not the past.

In a clear, strong voice, she began. "I was taking a shortcut through the alley between the two strip malls this morning—"

Graham had his pad out, but he wasn't writing. The sound

of her voice was enough to brand the information she was reciting into his brain. "What time?" he interjected without looking at her.

"Early," Caitlin snapped.

Blowing out a breath, she paused to collect herself. It was bad enough having seen what she had without having Graham standing here, toppling down the rest of her life as if it were a pile of children's building blocks.

With renewed control she continued. "I didn't look at my watch, but it must have been before seven." She remembered glancing at the digital clock on her dashboard as she had rounded the corner to the empty lot. It had read 6:42. The clock was off, but not by much. "It was," she added. "Just."

Before seven. She had liked to sleep in, Graham remembered. It had taken all his persuasive powers to get her to watch the sunrise with him one Saturday. They had sat on the edge of a ridge and she had leaned her head against his shoulder, stifling a yawn.

He shook off the memory. "What were you doing in the alley that early?"

His voice was so cold, so angry. As if he had reason to blame her for something. *Why, Gray? Didn't the money last you long enough? Is that why you're angry?*

She raised her chin defensively. "I was coming in to do inventory before the shop opened." She gestured toward the front of the store, the tips of her fingers hitting the light yellow curtain. "In case you haven't noticed, the city is repaving the parking lot in front of my store, so I had to park my car three blocks away. I was taking a shortcut." Except it didn't turn out to be that short.

Graham nodded, but said nothing.

It annoyed her more than she could say, though she couldn't explain why, even to herself. Like a wounded animal, bent on self-preservation, she looked toward Jeffers. The encouraging expression on his face urged her on.

"I heard raised voices, two men arguing. And then..." She paused, her voice growing small as she attempted to distance herself from the horror she had seen. If she framed it as a scene from a bad movie, she could handle it. Caitlin began again. "And then I saw the taller man shoot the other one." She swallowed. "It was just a pop." Like a firecracker, she thought. Like something harmless. Except that it wasn't. "He must have had a silencer on it. It didn't sound like a gun at all."

Jeffers raised his brows. "Are you familiar with the way guns sound?" The question was so casually stated, it took her a moment to assimilate it.

"She used to go to the handgun range," Graham answered for her. His voice was as quiet as the calm before the storm.

Caitlin frowned, hating the intrusion. Hating the fact that he knew anything about her. That he knew everything and had still left.

"My father wanted me to know my way around guns to protect myself," she explained to Jeffers a little too quickly, trying to blot out the sound of Graham's voice from her head.

Jeffers took the information down. "Against anything in particular?"

The smile on Graham's face had no underpinnings. "Undesirables."

His tone was mild, belying the pain that shimmered just beneath, the pain he had thought he'd come to terms with a long time ago. He had always known that there was no point in harboring bitterness within his soul. Bitterness just ate away at you, eroding you like the steady drip of battery acid. It dishonored his way of life. It annoyed him that a trace of it was still there, after all this time.

His dark brown eyes shifted to her blue ones and held for a small piece of eternity.

From where Jeffers stood, it looked like a contest of wills. Very deliberately he cleared his throat again. It took longer to get their attention this time.

Caitlin dragged her eyes away, toward Jeffers. He couldn't read them. "Getting back to this morning—?" He waited for her to continue with her story.

She shrugged. There wasn't much to add. "I ran," she said simply.

Good survival instincts. Lots of people froze with fear in adverse situations, like people in the path of oncoming cars who stood rooted as the vehicle sped toward them. "Did you get a good look at him?"

An image flashed through her mind. The man holding the gun. Firing. The other man crumpling. She tried to summon the other's face, but it refused to materialize.

"Not really. Just part of his profile." She wished there had been more. No one deserved to die like that, in an alley, no matter what he had done. "The man with the gun had his back to me for most of it."

From Graham's perspective there was a more important question that had been left unasked. "Did he see *you?*"

Reluctantly Caitlin looked at Graham again. His question sounded almost like an accusation. What right did he have to even be here? Detective or no detective, if he had a shred of decency left within him, he would have taken himself off the case as soon as he knew she was involved.

Had curiosity urged him on to come see just what he had thrown away so cavalierly in exchange for fifty thousand dollars?

A lot, Graham. You threw away a lot.

She raised her eyes to him defiantly, barely holding on to her anger. She told herself that was all it was. Only anger. No more hurt, no more pain. Those feelings, along with the love she'd had for him, were dead.

She shook her head. "I don't think he saw me."

She didn't think so. But there was always a chance. Graham didn't like leaving anything to chance. Chance was far too whimsical to suit him. If the killer had seen her and thought she had seen him...

He didn't like the direction his thoughts were taking.

Damn, any second they were going to draw pistols and aim, Jeffers thought. He laid a settling hand on Caitlin's arm, drawing her attention away from the line of fire. "Would you be up to coming in and looking at some mug shots for us?"

She didn't think there was much point in that. And she was

behind in her schedule as it was. "I already told you, I really didn't get that good a look."

Jeffers nodded, his voice mild, soothing. The way he saw it, there was a great deal of damage control required here.

"I understand, but sometimes memories can be jarred by outside influences." Without meaning to, he glanced at Graham, the action underscoring his words. "You know how it is."

"Yes," Caitlin agreed quietly. "I know how it is. All right, I'll go. Let me just get my purse."

"Take as much time as you'd like," Jeffers encouraged, his smile light. He debated his next move, then made up his mind. "Would you excuse us for a moment?"

Caitlin nodded, relieved by the unexpected, momentary respite.

Jeffers was already turning toward his partner. "Mind if I have a word with you, Gray?"

Graham didn't answer. Instead, he turned on the heel of his well-worn boot and started walking. He continued walking until he was just outside the entrance to the store.

Standing before the door, he took a deep breath, savoring it like a man who had been in danger of suffocating. The air was hot. Yet it was still better than being inside, breathing in her fragrance, sharing the air with her.

Jeffers circled Graham until he stood in front of his partner. Silence was a tool in Graham's hands. He could use it and be more comfortable with it than anyone Jeffers had ever known.

But silence gave him no answers and he wanted them. Jeffers gestured behind him toward the shop. "What the hell was going on in there?"

Fathomless eyes regarded Jeffers for a long moment, undercutting his annoyance.

"We're handling an investigation," Graham answered in the same mild tone he would have used in announcing the temperature. "If you don't know that by now, I'd say the city's wasting its money on you."

He was in no mood for drollness. "The hell with the city.

You know what I mean." Jeffers moved closer, lowering his voice as two women, walking into the store, regarded him with passing interest. "I've never seen two people cross swords like that. It was like being in the middle of *Star Wars* with Luke Skywalker and Darth Vader battling it out with light sabers. I felt like I was going to be cut down at any second by a stray blow."

A hint of amusement entered Graham's eyes. "Then you should have moved."

Jeffers let out an exasperated sigh. Gray wasn't going to volunteer anything. Not unless he asked him point-blank. So what else was new? Gray was more close-mouthed than a statue when he wanted to be. And he obviously wanted to be now.

Asking never bothered Jeffers. "Where do you know this woman from?"

Graham banked down a wave of memories that threatened to engulf him. He didn't want to remember. Any of it. "From a long time ago."

Jeffers shrugged haplessly. "Talkative as usual." Whether Gray gave him an explanation or not, this woman had obviously gotten under his skin. And they were partners. That meant understanding without knowing why. "You want me to take over the case, Gray? I can get Munoz to work with me."

Graham had never asked anyone to cut him slack before, and he wasn't about to start now, though he appreciated the offer. The corners of his mouth lifted slightly. "No, I can handle it. Thanks."

The last word did a lot to erase the annoyance Jeffers had felt at being shut out. He sighed. "You know, it'd be nice if you shared once in a while."

They did, Graham thought. More than he would have guessed they would when he had first been matched with the feisty detective.

"We spend time together, Ben, off and on the force." He looked at Jeffers pointedly. "Don't get in my face about this."

Jeffers raised his hands in the universal sign of surrender. "Consider your face abandoned." He knew that if and when Gray wanted to talk, he would. If he didn't, nothing he could say was going to force Redhawk to take him into his confidence. "Have it your way, Chief."

The slight curve transformed into a grin. "I usually do, paleface."

Ben Jeffers was as good a friend as he could have asked for. He hadn't meant to snap at him. Seeing Caitlin again after all these years had brought back a myriad of emotions he thought he had gotten over long ago.

Some things, he mused as he turned and walked into the store again, a man just never got over. He supposed that included his first love. Graham paused, holding the door open until Jeffers followed him inside.

Caitlin was standing in the store, he noted, talking to a customer. A mild relief whispered through him. He hadn't wanted to reenter that cubicle. Not while she was in it. Though what they had once had was dead, he didn't believe in masochism.

"Ms. Cassidy," he said formally as he approached her. "Are you ready to come downtown with us?"

He saw the annoyed look flash in her eyes as the woman next to her exchanged glances with another customer. The older woman, clutching an absurd scrap of red material, placed a motherly hand on Caitlin's arm.

"Is anything wrong, dear?"

Too bad Caitlin's mother hadn't been like that, he thought. Maybe if Caitlin hadn't been raised by a piranha, things might have turned out differently for them.

Caitlin shook her head, her smile wide and surprisingly genuine, Graham thought, for one he assumed was just pasted on. Her eyes became steely only when she turned them on him. "The detectives just want me to look at their collection of photographs." She nodded at the teddy the woman had decided on. "You enjoy that and let me know how your husband liked it on you. Have a happy anniversary."

"I will," she promised, blushing.

Graham saw Jeffers raise a brow in his direction, but his expression remained professional and unchanged. For his part, Graham didn't understand why women wasted so much money on things no one saw.

Caitlin focused her attention on Jeffers. She was determined to avoid looking at Graham as much as was humanly possible.

This entire episode had shaken her up more than she was willing to admit. Having Graham appear out of nowhere after all this time made things that much worse. She was beginning to wonder if Kerry had been right. Maybe she would have been better off not reporting this to the police. They would have discovered the body soon enough and it wasn't as if she could make a positive ID of the man who had fired the gun. Not from a glimpse of a profile.

"Will this take long, Detective Jeffers?"

Jeffers offered her his most reassuring smile. "Not long at all." Time, after all, was a relative thing.

He stepped ahead of her quickly and held the door open. Graham scowled at him. Hand on the door, he waited until Jeffers walked out before following.

He'd had a feeling this was going to be a bad day when he'd woken up this morning. There had been a crow right outside his window. He was too much of a Navajo not to have a healthy respect for omens.

Caitlin walked out ahead of the two men, resigned to the ordeal. With all her heart she wished that she had been just a little earlier this morning. Or a good deal later.

Or, at the very least, that Graham was somewhere in California, where she had believed him to be.

Caitlin quickly discovered that a squad room was not a quiet place. All sorts of people came and went in a continuous reshuffling of humanity. Very noisy people.

Caitlin found it difficult to concentrate on the small, stark black-and-white photographs arranged before her. A grim collection of lives gone astray. It was difficult to concentrate because of the noise, because the faces in the photographs were all beginning to look alike and because her thoughts perversely insisted on straying.

It was as if someone had fused a kaleidoscope to her mind. With every turn of her head, with every pass of an unguarded moment, another scene from her past would wink in and out.

Scenes with Graham, reminding her that once she had believed that her life had begun the first day that he had walked into it.

She sighed. She'd been stupid, very stupid. Seventeen seemed more than twelve years in the past. It was more like an aeon.

Caitlin moved her shoulders, subtly stretching muscles that were beginning to cramp. It was no use. She wanted to help, but she was getting nowhere. Sighing again, she closed the book and placed it on top of the other two that she had fruitlessly pored over.

It was getting late. She had already given the police artist as much of a description as she could recall. There wasn't anything to be accomplished by remaining any longer. She had to get back to the shop. Back to the shop and away from here. She was all too aware that Graham was sitting just two desks away and that he had been watching her.

Graham glanced up from his desk as if the sound of Caitlin's sigh had caught his attention. As if he'd had his mind on something other than her for the past hour. Try as he might, he couldn't seem to focus on anything beyond the woman sitting by the window. Ben had disappeared about fifteen minutes ago, after placing the last book on the desk. Munoz had said something about the desk sergeant wanting to see him.

So much for his shock absorber.

She was restless, he thought, studying her face. And tired. With an inner sigh of his own, Graham rose and made his way over.

He nodded at the pile of books with mug shots. "No luck?"

She tried to pretend that she didn't know him, that he was

a stranger like the other detective. She wanted to be civil and this was the only way.

"Afraid not." Caitlin pushed the last book back with the tip of her finger, straightening it on the stack. She raised her eyes to his face. "Anything else you want me to look at?"

Graham slowly shook his head. He had figured this would be an exercise in futility. She had already said she'd only caught a glimpse of a profile. Not exactly a sterling eyewitness, he thought, although, as he remembered it, she had an eye for detail that was better than most people's.

"I don't think there's much point in it, do you?" he said finally.

Why did she feel as if they were talking about something else? As if there was something to talk about? She knew there wasn't.

Caitlin shook her head. "No, I don't." She wet her lips as she glanced at the door. She missed the effect that the small, meaningless gesture had on him. "I'd like to go home, if you don't mind."

"I don't mind at all." The deadly calm in his voice had her looking at him again. "I stopped minding a long time ago." Maybe it was petty, but he wanted her to know that, to know that he had ceased to care.

There was a flicker of anger in her eyes before they went completely flat. Did he think he was telling her something new? Her mother had made it all too clear to her when she had given her Graham's message. Graham's "love" had had a price tag on it.

"Yes, I know."

Graham felt his own flash of anger, though his expression never changed. Now, what the hell was that supposed to mean? She'd been the one to walk out, not him. What gave her the right to take that accusing tone with him?

With effort, Graham reminded himself that he didn't care anymore. The past was dead, gone. There was no point in letting it rankle the present.

Irritated, he looked around for Ben. His partner was nowhere to be seen within the press of milling bodies in the squad room. Damn. Graham ran a hand along the back of his neck. "I'll take you back."

She didn't want to be anywhere near him. Caitlin picked up her shoulder bag and defiantly dropped the strap onto her shoulder, a soldier going off to war. "Don't trouble yourself. I'll call a cab."

She always had been a stubborn woman. He didn't relish the thought of being in yet another confining place with her, but there were rules to follow. You put witnesses back where you found them. This included irritating females and specters from the past.

"I said I'll take you back—" he fairly growled out the words "—so just hang on." He crossed to the sign-out board and chalked in his destination.

Caitlin stared at his broad back.

I would have hung on, you damn jerk, if you had been willing to.

God, but she was rattled. Caitlin dragged a hand through her hair. "I have to go now," she insisted, wanting to be rid of him. Just seeing him was like opening up a gaping wound that had never healed properly. "I've already missed too much of the morning."

He turned in time to see her drop her hand to her side. It was shaking. It wasn't every day that she got to witness a murder. He softened a little.

"Yeah," he agreed softly. "It's probably been a hell of a morning for you." He couldn't keep a hint of sarcasm out of his voice, despite the wave of sympathy that had passed through him.

Narrowing, her eyes met his. *You are a cold bastard,* they said. "Yes, it has and I'd like to put it behind me. All of it," she added pointedly.

He nodded. "Despite the fact that you are good at that, I don't think you can right at this moment." Taking his jacket from the back of his chair, he pushed the chair against his desk. "We'll be getting back to you with any suspects we come up with."

She wanted to know just what he had meant by that initial

crack, but let it go. She didn't want to dig up any more of the past than she was forced to endure. After what she'd witnessed this morning, Caitlin wasn't certain just what her breaking point was.

Up until four hours ago, she would have said that she was a very strong woman. Now she wasn't so sure.

Graham shoved his arms through the jacket that regulations dictated he keep available. There were times he wished that the captain would lighten up. Right at this moment, everything bothered him. And would continue to do so until he got Caitlin back to the shop.

Refraining from taking her arm, a move neither one of them would have appreciated, he nodded toward the door. "Let's go."

They were almost out of the squad room when someone called his name. "Hey, Redhawk!"

Graham turned. Chambers was holding up the telephone, waving it to and fro.

"It's for you," he called out above the din in the room. "They must have transferred it to my extension by mistake. It's your son. He says it's urgent."

Jake thought everything was urgent. Maybe at seven, everything was. Graham couldn't remember that far back.

Graham glanced toward Caitlin and saw a look he couldn't quite read in her eyes. He shrugged it off. "I've got to take that. Stay right here—I'll be with you in a couple of minutes." He tossed the last part over his shoulder.

"Sure," she murmured.

A son. He had a son.

And a wife.

Caitlin felt something constrict within her chest before she pushed it away. It made no difference to her if he was married or not.

Chapter 3

Taking the receiver from Chambers, Graham turned so that he could still see Caitlin. She looked out of place standing in the squad room, like a hothouse flower carelessly tossed into the swamp.

Looks were deceiving.

He leaned the receiver against his ear and shoulder. "Okay, Jake, make this quick, I'm in the middle of something. What's up?"

He heard a quick intake of breath before his son launched into his tale. "She says I have to make my bed and pick up my toys before I can go to Joey's house." Annoyance vibrated in the high-pitched voice.

Graham took the receiver into his hand again. "'She'?" he echoed, lowering his voice. "Who's 'she'?"

There was an audible sigh on the other end. Graham could almost see the frown materializing on his son's face. "Grandma."

Graham wasn't aware that he was nodding. He also didn't see Caitlin edging closer to him, drawn by an ungovernable curiosity.

"Good, she has a name, right? Grandma," he repeated. "Use it."

"Okay." Jake's controlled tone brought to mind Native Americans of old, sitting around campfires, working out peace-treaty compromises. He began to restate his problem. "Grandma said that I couldn't—"

Graham didn't have time to get into a long-winded story. Jake had already given him enough of a summary. "Grandma's got a point."

"Da-a-ad." Jake drew the name out until it had three syllables.

Graham grinned. Small for his age, Jake was feisty, ready to argue over any perceived injustice and just as ready to forgive and love. Half-Navajo, half-white—like Graham himself—Jake had entered his home when he'd been less than a week old. And had entered his heart shortly thereafter. Jake couldn't have been more his if the boy had come from his own seed.

"Hey, rules are there to follow." He glanced at Chambers's blotter. A rap sheet on a two-time loser mingled with a worn program Chambers had picked up at the last Phoenix Suns game and a candy bar. The rap sheet had a coffee stain in the corner. "Wait until she sends you off for a three-day fast."

"What?" Horror was infused into every letter of the word.

Graham laughed. When he was growing up, his world had been crammed with his mother's mysticism and symbols from the past. So crammed that he had rebelled against it, not knowing what it was he was turning his back on. No one was going to make Jake go through that if he didn't want to. Heritage didn't mean anything if it had to be rammed down your throat. It had to be subtly taught.

He suspected his mother had learned that. Finally.

"Nothing for you to worry about," he assured his son.

Time to wrap it up. Anticipation, or perhaps foreboding, nudged through his veins as he glanced over his shoulder toward Caitlin. Was it his imagination, or was she standing a lot closer than she had been?

"Jake, things go a lot smoother if you cooperate and stop

trying to wheedle your way out of things. In the time you spent arguing and being stubborn, you could have picked up half of your things.''

''Yeah, maybe.''

''Maybe'' in Jake's world was a face-saving way of saying yes. Satisfied, Graham shifted his weight, letting one of the detectives pass. Chambers pointed to the receiver, indicating that he wanted his telephone back.

''Okay. Now give me your grandmother for a minute.'' He waited, looking at the scantily dressed woman Valdez was leading to his desk. The populace of Phoenix had to be bored, looking for ways to entertain itself. This made three prostitutes in one day. That exceeded their usual complement by two.

It was going to be a long, hot summer, Graham speculated.

''Yes?''

His mother's voice, soft, wispy, had Graham automatically straightening his shoulders. His mother, first daughter of her tribe's medicine man, was a small-boned woman who stood only a few inches taller than her grandson, but there was an aura about her that commanded respect. Even from a six-two police detective. Especially if that police detective happened to be her son.

''I talked to Jake for you. He'll do what you tell him.'' He nodded at Chambers, who was giving him the sign to wrap it up.

Lily Redhawk expected nothing less. ''As it should be.''

She had been rigid while he was growing up. So rigid he had run away three times before he was into his teens. It had taken a long time for him to understand his mother. Almost as long as it had taken for him to come to terms with what he was. An outcast on the cusp of society.

They had both mellowed. He could talk to her now. ''And Ma? Lighten up on him a little, will you? It's summer.''

''Work still has to be done, Graham, whatever the season.''

He knew she loved the boy. He also knew, from his own experience, that it was difficult for her to show it. ''But the world won't end if his bed's not made.''

Graham could almost hear what his mother was thinking. How often had she told him that the spirit was guided by many factors, all of which had to be in place for a boy to move on the right path as he reached manhood. Her dissatisfaction was apparent in her voice. "Small child, small deeds. Larger child, larger—"

"I've got the picture, Ma. Look to your heart and do what you have to do. I'll see you tonight."

Graham hung up after her murmured assurance that she would be there, as usual. His mother had moved in shortly after Celia had walked out on him. There were many things about his mother that surprised him. None had surprised him more than that. He had needed and she had come. Somehow, she had known without his saying a word. It gave him a healthy respect for her ceremonies and what she believed was her connection with the spirit world.

Whatever worked, he mused.

Raising his eyes from the telephone, Graham saw Caitlin looking at him. She had a strange expression on her face, as if she was observing something unusual, something she couldn't understand. Idly he wondered what she was thinking, and why he should even care.

She hadn't meant to eavesdrop. It had just happened. Even with the din, she had overheard him. The words had been formal; the tone hadn't. Talking to his son, he had behaved exactly the way she had once envisioned him behaving.

Without meaning to, Caitlin was envious of the people on the other end of the line. Of his family. They brought out a gentler side of him. There were softer edges to Graham when he spoke to his son.

Caitlin wondered what sort of a woman he had married. And if he was happy.

Let it go, Cait. It's in the past. It doesn't matter anymore.

She squared her shoulders and glanced at her watch for his benefit before raising her eyes to his.

She had always had beautiful eyes, he thought as he approached her. Turquoise, like the jewelry his mother prized.

"Ready?"

Caitlin nodded and turned toward the outer door. It was hot in here. The squad room was beginning to smell musty to her as the press of bodies increased.

She stopped at the swinging door, automatically waiting for him. "How old is your boy?"

Graham pushed the door open and held it for her. He didn't bother asking how she knew about Jake. "Seven."

"Seven," she echoed. She tried to imagine him as a father of a seven-year-old and, despite the telephone conversation, had trouble conjuring up the image. "I guess he's a handful, then, if he's anything like you."

Graham inclined his head. The black-and-white floor leading to the main entrance was checkered with scars no amount of wax could disguise. He was aware of everything. Mainly, he was aware of Caitlin walking beside him. "He has his moments."

He pushed open the heavy double door for her. It was like stepping into an oven. Heat shimmered up from the pavement like wisps of faded mirages. He didn't have to look to find his car. It was parked in the same place it always was, day in, day out. It was the only place near the building large enough to accommodate the vehicle. The other detectives knew enough to leave it free.

"That way." Graham had to stop himself from taking her elbow. Old habits were attempting to resurface as if they hadn't been dormant for more than ten years. It had taken him a year to get over her. A year he had no intentions of reliving. Sliding one hand into his pocket, he gestured with the other toward his car.

He didn't bother breaking stride.

Caitlin stared, fascinated, as she fairly trotted next to him to keep up. He had to be kidding.

"The pink one?" Disbelief framed the question and she glanced at him, waiting for a disclaimer.

"The pink one," he confirmed.

She was amazed that there wasn't a hint of embarrassment in his voice.

The car, a '59 Eldorado Biarritz, was in gleaming mint

condition. It was a convertible, but he had the top up. Less sun damage that way. Parked on the far side of the building, it stood out amid the other cars like a giant in the midst of a tribe of pygmies.

Caitlin stopped at the passenger door, then raised her eyes to Graham's. She was apparently waiting for either the punch line or a lengthy explanation. Did she think he was driving the car on a dare?

When he remained silent, she asked, "Why?"

He would have thought that was self-evident. Graham lightly ran his palm along the chrome handle before unlocking it. "Because it's rare. There were only one thousand, three hundred and twenty made. And because it's beautiful."

He said it the way a lover spoke of his mistress. The way, she recalled without wanting to, he had once spoken to her.

Maybe the car would have better luck than she had, Caitlin thought sarcastically.

Graham opened the door for her and, after a moment, she got in. The seat gave, like a loving old friend, accepting her. "Doesn't this stick out a little in the neighborhood?"

He rounded the long hood and slid in behind the steering wheel. "A little."

If she looked closely, she could detect a hint of a smile on his face. Was he pulling her leg? "How do you do surveillance in a car like this?"

"I don't. We usually take one of the department's cars, the way we did when we went to your shop. But it comes in handy." As he spoke, he glided his hand over the dashboard.

Caitlin watched, and remembered. Self-conscious, she lowered her eyes.

He put the key into the ignition and then glanced over his shoulder to make sure the path was clear. It was. "People don't expect a policeman to be driving something quite so—"

She stared at the hood. There seemed to be miles of car in front of them. And miles more behind. It was like being in a tank. A pink tank.

"Gaudy?" she suggested.

"Obvious," he corrected.

"I see."

Caitlin settled back in the seat as Graham started the car. She expected to hear gears groaning in protest. Half the time her car sounded as if someone had let loose a chain saw inside it when she turned it on. Instead, the pink Cadillac purred into life.

The way she once had, beneath that same hand.

Attempting to clear her mind, Caitlin blew out a breath. The ride was so smooth that if she closed her eyes she couldn't tell that they were actually moving out of the lot. But eyes closed or not, she couldn't forget that she was sitting beside Graham. Though they weren't touching, she could feel his presence engulfing her.

"So," she began a little too brightly, a little too forced, "you've acquired a career, a car, so to speak—" she didn't bother hiding the smile that rose to her lips "—and a family since I last saw you." She slanted a glance in his direction. "You've been busy."

You didn't hurt at all, did you, Gray? Not like me. Damn you. She struggled to maintain an impersonal expression. If he could seem unaffected, so could she.

He spared her a look. Only the tight hold on the steering wheel warned him that his feelings were rising to the surface. He consciously relaxed his fingers.

"So have you. The store yours?" Naughty But Nice. It seemed fitting.

The store was her pride and joy. It was a nice, safe topic. "Yes, the store's mine."

"Doing well?" The car in front of him was doing twenty in a forty-five-mile zone. Graham signaled and switched lanes. "Although, I guess that wouldn't matter."

His comment got under her skin. She looked at him, wanting to jump on something, wanting to vent the wronged feeling inside her. "Why? Why wouldn't it matter?"

She sounded offended. He lifted a shoulder carelessly, then let it drop. "It's not as though you needed the money."

Money. She wondered how high a priority it held in his

life these days. It certainly had been paramount once. "Maybe I need the respect it affords me."

Full, sensuous lips pulled back into almost a grin. "Lingerie?"

Was he ridiculing her? The way her mother had when she had learned about the undertaking? Indignation coaxed the words from her. "Earning my own way."

As if she had to. He raised a brow. "What's the matter, mother cut you off?"

She heard the animosity. She supposed he had a right. God knew she did.

"No, I cut her off." There was surprise on his face when he turned to look at her, but he said nothing, waiting for an explanation. Caitlin sighed. Maybe in some strange way she owed him this much. "If she didn't control the purse strings, she couldn't feel as if she could control me." Caitlin shrugged. "Or, at least, that was the message I was attempting to send."

Her mother would always think she could control her life. Regina Cassidy felt she had the God-given right to control everyone's life. Manipulation had always been second nature to her.

Graham waited for an opening, then maneuvered his car back into the right lane. He had to make a right turn at the next corner. "Then how did you get the store?"

He was conscious of her sitting up a little straighter in her seat. "My father left me some money in his will when he died." Jonathan Cassidy had hardly ever opposed his wife outright, but he still knew what she was like. "It didn't all go to Mother."

The revelation took him by surprise. He'd known that Cassidy was ill, but he hadn't thought it was anything serious. "He died?"

"Yes."

Even now, after all this time, she could feel tears gathering at the mention of her father's death. Jonathan Cassidy had been the only one to understand her, to understand that she wanted to be free of her mother's social whirl. Of her mother's social web. He'd been diagnosed with pancreatic cancer midway through her senior year and died six months later, thinking she was going to marry Graham. Caitlin hadn't had the heart to tell him otherwise. By the time Graham had left her, her father was too weak to upset.

But, oh, she could have used his support then. He was the only one she could have talked through the pain with. She'd had to do it all on her own.

She had gone on a trip to Paris. The one she had meant to surprise Graham with. She had wanted to give him Paris for their honeymoon.

"He died the summer I graduated." Her voice was stoic as she stared straight ahead.

He remembered a kind, patrician-looking man with prematurely silver hair and an easy laugh. Jonathan Cassidy had been the kind of father he would have chosen for his own, if he had been allowed.

Graham glanced at Caitlin. Her profile was rigid. She probably didn't take sympathy any better than he did, though that surprised him.

He thought of that last day. Well, maybe it didn't surprise him at that. He really knew very little about her.

"I'm sorry. I liked him." He turned the corner and took advantage of the break in traffic by speeding up. They were almost there.

"He liked you, too." But then, her father hadn't known of Graham's darker side. Or his more shallow side, she amended.

The silence lingered, oppressive, as loud as war drums within the car. He let it go on for a block. "You don't see much of your mother now?"

Caitlin shrugged. "We get together once a month or so, if she happens to be on this side of the continent." They each kept cursory contact for their own reasons. Love had little to do with it. Obligation and duty were the operative words.

She smiled to herself. What would her mother say if she knew her daughter was getting a ride back to the store from Graham Redhawk? Plenty, if she knew her mother.

"After Daddy died, she indulged herself in travel. There

always seems to be a party somewhere she needs to attend.''
It was a way of life that held absolutely no interest for Caitlin.

"And you?" Graham figured that would be Caitlin's chosen place, at her mother's side entertaining. That was the picture Regina Cassidy had painted for him that last day.

"You're making her turn her back on what's rightfully hers," Regina had informed him coldly. "If you marry her, I'll see to it that she's disowned."

But it was Caitlin's own words that had made up his mind for him.

Caitlin shook her head, still attempting to concentrate on something other than the few inches that separated them. "I'm too busy working to party."

Jamming on his brakes, Graham swore under his breath as a dark sports car cut him off.

Caitlin suppressed a laugh at the look on his face. "This thing is large enough to block an entire intersection." She looked at him before letting her glance drift over the interior of the car. "What made you buy it?"

He doubted she could understand his passion for the Eldorado. The car, like him, had to make its own place in a world that was too streamlined, too fast paced to appreciate things that were different.

"It's a classic. I always liked classic-looking things." He spared her a long glance just before the light turned green.

His words felt like a warm caress and a slap in the face at the same time.

"So you once said."

Damn, why was he affecting her like this? Why was he affecting her at all, especially after all this time? She wished her shop was located closer to the precinct, or better yet that she had insisted on taking a cab. Then he couldn't have strong-armed her into letting him drive her back to her store.

She searched for something to talk about that didn't dredge up memories with both hands. "Think you'll catch the guy who shot that man?"

They were on his terrain now. Familiar territory. The tension eased from his spine. But not his shoulders. "There's a fifty-fifty chance."

Well, at least he was being honest with her. No one quoted odds like that and boasted about them. "That low?"

"Hey, those are good odds." It all depended on how you looked at things. "Crime shows to the contrary, the bad guy usually goes free." He felt rather than saw her involuntary shiver. He hadn't been trying to frighten her. He was so accustomed to the danger that lived on the streets he walked, he hadn't thought how such knowledge might affect someone else. "Worried?"

"Who, me?" She wanted to laugh it off, but didn't quite attain the desired effect. Her smile faded. "Maybe just a little."

He did what he could to make amends. No one deserved to live in fear. "Whoever did it is probably sitting at a bus station right now with a ticket to Somewhere Else, U.S.A., clutched in his hand."

She'd like to believe that. Would like to believe that they would either catch whoever had done it or that the man would vanish, never to turn up again.

She bit her lower lip as she turned toward Graham. "You think?"

With practiced ease Graham pulled up a few blocks away from her shop, guiding the wide car into a parking space that just barely accommodated it.

Shutting off the engine, he looked at her. She could still wring things from him the way no one else could, even after all that had passed between them.

"I think," he assured her. Digging into the breast pocket of his jacket, he pulled out a small card and handed it to her. "If you want to talk, or you remember anything else about this morning, call me."

Caitlin glanced at the card. It had his name and the precinct number on it. All very professional. She slipped it into her purse, an annoying ache building in her chest.

"You're probably right," she agreed. "The man's probably gone." She said it to convince herself, and they both knew it. "What are you going to do now? About the case," she qualified quickly, afraid that he might misconstrue her question. She had no personal desire to know what he was doing.

The procedure was standard. He recited it for her. "Question people in the neighborhood. See if anyone's seen or heard anything relevant. We'll pass around that sketch Nathan drew from your initial input," he said, mentioning the police artist. "The killer might have been in the neighborhood earlier."

Caitlin nodded, feeling oddly weak-kneed. The implications of the case were finally settling in like a heavy, wet army blanket. It hadn't been a movie this morning. It had been real life. And she had witnessed it.

Her face suddenly paled. For a moment he thought she was going to faint. Without thinking, he took her arm to steady her.

"Hey, it's going to be all right," he said gruffly. He didn't know how to offer sympathy. Not to her. Not with the ghost of summers past hovering between them in the car. But he didn't like the fear that he had glimpsed in her eyes, either.

"Sure it is." Abruptly she opened the door and stepped out as if the seat had suddenly caught fire. She didn't want to think about anything. Not about Graham, not about the dead man and not about the man who had shot him. She just wanted her life back, the way it had been yesterday. Organized. Orderly. It had taken her a long time to achieve that state, building it out of the shattered pieces he had left behind.

She didn't even say goodbye. She just turned and walked away from the car. Quickly.

Graham sat for a moment and watched Caitlin until she disappeared behind a building. Then he dragged both hands through his hair and let out a deep breath. Her scent was in the car. He rolled down the windows and started the engine again.

He had work to do.

"Let's go, Esmerelda." He threw the car into Reverse and pulled out of the spot.

The day had been one of the longest ones of Graham's career. He and Jeffers had hit the streets shortly after he had returned to the precinct. Armed with flyers, they had canvassed the area, asking local store owners if they had seen or heard anything unusual. Taking into account the early hour of the crime, it seemed improbable that anyone had.

He hadn't been disappointed.

As was expected, the dead man had had no wallet on him, but his fingerprints had given them a name. Joshua Landers. And a priors sheet had given them a few local leads to pursue.

At least it was something.

What Graham wanted when he walked through the door of his one-story, white stucco house was a good meal and a little companionship from his son.

And maybe for the Colorado Rockies to finally win a game.

Empathy with underdogs had him rooting for a team that hadn't a prayer of having a winning season or even coming within a hundred miles of a .500 average. He figured that gave them something in common.

What he didn't want was more trouble or problems of any sort.

Jake was sprawled out on the sofa, his eyes glued to the twenty-inch television that, along with his grandmother's two-faced weaves on the opposite wall, dominated the room.

Graham closed the door behind him and locked it automatically. "Hi, Jake, how's it going?" He nodded at the set.

Jake looked at his father glumly as he sat up. "They're losing."

He laughed quietly. Winning baseball games was of the utmost importance to Jake. The concept of competition wasn't part of Navajo culture, but Jake was very much a nineties kind of child.

"Some things are dependable." Graham pocketed his key. "Grandma around?"

Jake nodded and pointed to the left, his eyes back on the screen. "In the kitchen."

Glancing at the score that flashed across the bottom of the screen as the side was retired, Graham followed the aroma to the kitchen. His stomach growled in hungry anticipation.

His mother was at the stove, stirring what was to be their dinner in a large metal pot. She was dressed in traditional Navajo costume—she claimed she was comfortable that way and no other. Graham had given up trying to change her.

He bent over her and pressed a kiss to her cheek. "Hi, Ma."

Lily Redhawk looked up at her only son. People generally mistook them for sister and brother rather than mother and son. But today her face, usually so peaceful, so youthful, looked drawn. She looked very close to her own age.

The table was set. All but the glasses. He took out three from the cupboard and placed one at each setting. "What's the matter, Ma? Jake still giving you a hard time?" Graham had thought that the matter had been settled this morning.

"Jake has been fine," she said quietly. "You had a call today."

He knew by the way she said it that he wasn't going to like this. "From?"

She placed the wooden spoon down on the stove. "Celia's lawyer."

The divorce had been final for almost two years. He sent money each month to a post office box because he didn't know where she was staying. It was better that way. He and Jake were managing very well without her.

He sat down and looked at his mother. "What does she want now?"

Lily glanced toward the other room. Her grandson was exactly where he had been for the past hour. Glued to the television set. It usually irritated her. For once, she was glad.

Her eyes returned to her son's face. Her own was grim. It mirrored the way she felt at having to be the one to give Graham the news.

"Jake."

Chapter 4

Graham stared at his mother. He refused to allow the meaning behind her words to penetrate beyond a certain point. The very thought of what she was saying made the breath stagnate in his lungs.

"Jake? What do you mean, Jake?"

Neither his mother's expression nor her tone changed. But he felt the undercurrent of sympathy nonetheless. It was evident in tiny gestures—an inclination of her head, the set of her shoulders. She felt for him. "Jake, your son. Celia wants custody of Jake."

He rose so quickly his chair toppled to the floor on its side. "Did the lawyer leave a number?"

"Yes." Graham already had the receiver in his hand, ready to dial. "He said he was leaving the office at five."

He knew it was past that now, yet he glanced at his watch anyway. Swearing, Graham replaced the receiver. No sense getting himself worked up now. There would be time enough for that in the morning.

The set of his mouth was grim as he picked up the chair and righted it. "She can't have him."

Lily knew how much the boy meant to him; how much, though she had resisted, Jake had come to mean to her. "We could go back to the reservation."

That had been her solution the last time, when her own marriage had crumbled before her eyes, injuring her young pride. She had returned with her small son, seeking the solace that familiarity afforded.

It hadn't given him the same sustenance. "You think they wouldn't find us on the reservation?" It would be the first place they would look.

The branches of her family spread over great distances. "In Utah."

He shook his head. He wasn't about to go into hiding, always looking over his shoulder. Always waiting for someone to catch up to him and Jake. There was a measure of that element in his job now; he wasn't about to go through that as a father.

"I'm fighting this, Ma, right here. On my own grounds."

She shrugged. "As you will."

Graham scrubbed his hands over his face. God, but he was tired, tired of fighting for everything he wanted. Tired of his ex-wife's vacillation. First she wanted to be a mother, then she didn't. Now she wanted to again. Couldn't she make up her mind?

He had married Celia because she had told him she was pregnant with his child. Honor had been very important to him, especially at that time. The wounds that Caitlin had left had just begun to heal. So he had given Celia his name and awaited the child with mixed feelings.

Celia had miscarried in her fifth month. The complications that followed had robbed her of the ability to ever conceive again. She'd been so distraught, he'd feared for her sanity. The prospect of emptiness had taken on monumental proportions for her and she'd begged him to agree to an adoption.

He hadn't wanted to. There was something within him that had resisted the idea of taking in another man's child. But she had pleaded and cried. In the end, he had agreed to adopt a half-Navajo baby. A half-breed, he had mused, like himself.

It was the best thing he had ever done. Jake represented the very best part of him. He loved the boy the way he couldn't allow himself to love anyone else. Without reservations.

And now she wanted to take him away.

His hand closed over the back of the wooden chair, tightening until his knuckles looked as if they would break through the skin. His eyes shifted to his mother's. "She can't have him," he repeated fiercely.

"Have who?"

Graham turned to see Jake walking into the kitchen. Jake was wearing one of Graham's old T-shirts that was legions too large for him. But his son liked wearing his old clothes. He said it gave him something to grow into.

Celia would have to kill him before she got the boy. "Nobody you know about." Playfully he pushed the brim of Jake's baseball cap down until it covered his eyes. He constrained his emotions behind a carefully constructed wall that he had built, brick by brick, over the long years of enduring the trials that life saw fit to throw people who were considered different. "What say we have dinner and then settle back and watch the end of the game?"

The television screen just barely visible behind Jake in the family room was blank. He'd turned it off in disgust. Jake waved a dismissive hand toward it. "Ah, it's hopeless."

Graham draped his arm around the slight shoulders. "Nothing," he commented a bit too fiercely, "is ever hopeless."

Maybe, Graham thought, catching the mildly surprised look on his mother's face, if he said it often enough he'd actually believe it.

Morning proved no better. Graham hadn't been able to reach Celia's lawyer. A very cool secretary had informed him that Mr. Wells was in court for the morning and that she would pass on his message to him.

Since he had no idea where Celia was, there was nothing to do but wait.

He felt antsy as he hung up the receiver. Maybe it was time

to send out feelers and try to locate her. He hadn't attempted to find her before because he honestly hadn't wanted to. He had remained married to Celia for Jake's sake. And for Jake's sake, he had given her the divorce she'd asked for when she had declared a need to find her identity. Jake deserved something better than to grow up listening to his parents constantly argue.

But he needed to know where she was now, needed to make a move. He wasn't the type to just sit back and wait for things to happen to him. He liked knowing the kinds of cards fate was dealing out. You couldn't make a countermove if you weren't prepared.

He glanced at the folder with Caitlin's name written across it. Another unexpected twist. Damn, but life was getting complicated.

"Have you seen this?" The question was punctuated by the thud of a newspaper falling on his desk. Jeffers stood next to him, frowning.

Graham didn't bother looking at the paper. Jeffers was always getting worked up over some political issue or other. Graham found it prudent not to get into those kinds of discussions with him.

"I haven't caught up to last month's news." Graham moved the folded section aside.

Just as smoothly, Jeffers moved the newspaper back. He stabbed a forefinger at the lower right-hand corner. "Read this."

Since Jeffers seemed so determined, Graham picked up the newspaper and glanced at the story, which barely represented five inches of print. Caitlin's name sprang up at him as if it had been highlighted by a yellow felt-tip marker. There wasn't much of a story, just enough to let the killer know that he had been seen and the identity of the person who had seen him.

Graham dropped the newspaper on his desk again. "Oh, God."

"Exactly." Jeffers nodded grimly, shoving his hands into

his pockets. The potential damage that those few lines of print could do was enormous.

Graham wondered if Caitlin had seen it yet. Or, more important, if the killer had. He began to reach for the telephone.

"Redhawk, Jeffers, in my office." Martinez's voice sliced through the din in the office like a sharp rapier. "Now."

Jeffers and Graham exchanged looks. "I guess he's seen the article, too," Jeffers muttered.

If there was any doubt, it was quickly dissipated when they walked into Martinez's office. The front page of today's paper was spread across the captain's desk. He closed the door before he turned to the men. His face was like a dark thundercloud just before it unleashed the rain.

Martinez pointed to the newspaper. "How did this get out?"

In reply, both men shrugged almost in unison. Jeffers's expression was one of total innocence. "They didn't get it from me."

Graham leaned a shoulder against the wall next to the door. Martinez knew better than to think he had anything to do with it. There was no love lost between him and the news media. He thought of them as little better than vultures, circling carrion. "Could have been anyone in the neighborhood after we circulated the flyers."

It was the most plausible explanation, but Martinez was far from happy about it. "The lamebrain who wrote this put her name in the article." He looked from one man to the other. "You know what that means."

Jeffers nodded. "She's going to need protection."

The captain's expression grew grimmer. "Yes, and we're shorthanded as it is." The city was in the midst of contract renegotiations with the police force. Talks had been suspended twice already and some of his men were calling in with what the press whimsically referred to as "the blue flu." It left him understaffed and overstressed.

Graham nodded, thinking of his own caseload. "Tell me something I don't know."

Martinez's eyes shifted to Graham. "All right, I'm assigning you to protect her."

If he winced in response, he was sure no one noticed. Graham looked toward his partner. "What about Jeffers?"

Both men were good, but Martinez believed that Redhawk had the edge. He'd had from the very first. Maybe he'd seen one too many Westerns as a kid, but there was something of the hunter about Redhawk that made Martinez feel more confident giving him the assignment.

"Jeffers'll touch base with you and relieve you periodically. I've got other priorities for him." He paused, vainly attempting to read the detective's expression. He thought he caught an undercurrent of some kind. "Something about this case you don't like?"

The slight movement of Graham's head was almost imperceptible. "No."

Martinez nodded once. "All right, then, it's settled. As of now, you're to consider yourself Cassidy's guardian angel."

Jeffers glanced at Graham and laughed. "It's damn hard picturing this ape with wings."

Graham turned only his eyes. "How would you like to be fitted for a harp?"

Jeffers got the message. He raised his hands chest level in mock surrender, then looked at his superior. "You know, if it's a small-time hood, the guy might have already left town."

Martinez had already considered that. "Yeah, or he might be looking to eliminate the only witness that he thinks can finger him. We can't take that chance. Vice just connected the dead man to a major drug cartel that's trying to establish itself here."

Jeffers looked more surprised than Graham. The dead man had been one of the city's vermin, a small-timer running afoul of the law since he'd been a minor. "That weasel?"

Martinez shrugged indifferently. "The pawns are always expendable." He turned toward Graham, his mind already on the next case. He had an even score on his desk to choose from, all of which should have been solved "yesterday." "If nothing happens in about two weeks, one way or the other, we'll back off.'' His eyes held Graham's pointedly. Damn, he wished he knew what was going on behind those dark eyes. ''I'd rather be overcautious than lose another citizen.''

Graham knew what he was referring to. The Saunders case. It had been entirely different from this one. The witness to a domestic-violence incident that had claimed the lives of two family members had been killed by the prime suspect's brother after the witness had picked out the former from a lineup. The police hadn't thought to give the witness protection, since the suspect was behind bars. The newspapers had practically crucified the department for what it declared to be their ''gross negligence.''

Nobody wanted a repeat performance, not in body count, not in printed words. Martinez waved the two men out of his office. ''All right, go earn your pay.''

Jeffers obligingly retreated. In the doorway, Graham slanted a look at his superior. ''I thought we just did, listening to you.''

Martinez muttered something unintelligible under his breath, then waved Graham out of his office.

Terrific. Caitlin's guardian angel. Just what he needed.

Jeffers was lingering at his desk when Graham reached it. Concern was written into the younger man's features. ''You want me to go back to the captain and ask to be assigned to the Cassidy woman instead of you?''

He wasn't about to ask for preferential treatment after Martinez had dismissed the mere suggestion. He laughed shortly, though the underlying humor in the situation escaped him at the moment. ''That obvious?''

''Hey, I could have toasted marshmallows in the fallout yesterday.'' He shoved his hands into his pockets and studied Graham's profile. Tension made it even more rocklike than usual. ''You any more in the mood to talk about it now?''

He knew curiosity was eating Jeffers up. Ben read mysteries starting with the back page first. But he was good at keeping secrets.

Graham dragged a hand through his hair, as if that could somehow loosen him up inside. He felt tight, wound up, like he was going to explode at any minute. "We were almost married once."

Jeffers wasn't exactly sure what he had expected to hear, but it wasn't that. "Wow. What happened?"

Graham looked idly through the folders on his desk. "It didn't work out," he said offhandedly. "It was a long time ago."

That much was obvious, Jeffers mused. "No amiable parting, huh?"

A dry laugh echoed in his throat. "No amiable parting."

Sympathy tugged at Jeffers. "Sure you don't want me to—?" He jerked a thumb in the direction of Martinez's office.

Graham shook his head. "Thanks for the offer, but there's nothing here I can't handle." He'd made up his mind to that a long time ago.

He picked up his sports jacket and slung it over his shoulder. "I'll check in with you later." He glanced at his phone. "Oh, and if I get in any calls, have them transferred to the number at the shop."

Jeffers wondered if Graham was working on something he hadn't bothered mentioning to him. Gray had a habit of going out on his own. "Sure. Expecting anything?"

"Yeah," he said quietly. He saw interest flicker in Jeffers's blue eyes. Looked as if it was a day for sharing. "Celia wants Jake."

Jeffers's jaw dropped. "Oh, hell."

That about summed it up, Graham thought. "My feelings exactly."

With a nod at his partner, Graham walked out the door.

It had been a busy morning at Naughty But Nice. This was their first lull in over an hour. So when the bell softly rang, announcing the entrance of another customer, Kerry looked up reluctantly from the display she was arranging.

For a second her heart stopped. Reaching over, she nudged Caitlin, who was on her knees behind the counter, looking for the last box of sachet.

"Uh-oh, storm warnings at six o'clock," Kerry whispered, her eyes riveted on the woman entering the store.

Caitlin rose, confused by the sobered expression on Kerry's normally animated face. She still felt jumpy after yesterday morning, though she had vehemently denied it when Kerry mentioned it.

"What are you babbling abou—?" Caitlin's heart sank as she looked toward the entrance.

A tall, regal woman, outfitted in designer originals from head to foot, was crossing the floor to them. Diamonds flashed from her hands and throat like tiny white bolts of light. Her eyes were a steely, uncompromising blue and they had targeted Caitlin, bent on intimidation at ten paces.

White-hot anger was imprinted on the delicate, aristocratic features. Her short, tawny hair was swept away from her face, emphasizing her expression.

Now what? Caitlin thought, a sinking feeling fighting for possession of her stomach.

Regina Cassidy slapped a newspaper down on the counter, sending a display of lacy panties raining down on the floor like a multitude of pastel snowflakes. The contempt that emanated from her encompassed the panties, the shop and her daughter.

"What do you mean by dragging our name through the mud?" Her voice, with its perfect diction, was as grating as a nail running along a chalkboard.

Kerry smiled broadly, knowing she made less than no impression on the woman. "Good morning, Mrs. Cassidy. Nice to see you again."

Regina spared Kerry one glare, the way she might an annoying mosquito, and then dismissed her as if she didn't exist.

Kerry took the opportunity to bow out, knowing that Caitlin would welcome the privacy. She ushered Eva to the back room with her.

A finely manicured scarlet nail tapped the bottom of the newspaper. Regina's eyes pinned her errant daughter. "Well?"

Caitlin was behind in her inventory work and her accounting. A shipment of negligees was overdue and she had lost a half day yesterday through no fault of her own. Holding on to the reins of her life was becoming increasingly difficult. Reading newspapers did not head the list of her priorities at the moment.

She ignored the tapping nail. "I don't know what you're talking about, Mother."

The blue eyes widened in disbelief. Now her daughter was adding lying to her list of offenses. "Oh, you don't?" Regina held up the paper, indicating the article. "Well, read!"

Annoyed at being treated like a child, Caitlin glanced at the newspaper and then drew in her breath. A clammy feeling slid over her, tightening spasmodically. The article was about the shooting she had witnessed. Whoever had written the story had put in her name.

Oh, God, wasn't this nightmare ever going to be over? She might as well have arrows pointing in her direction for the killer's benefit.

How could anyone have been so stupid, so heartless? Wasn't her safety worth more than a byline on a page that would line some bird's cage tomorrow?

With effort, Caitlin gathered her dignity. Her mother wouldn't understand anything she was going through. Or any of the reasons that had prompted her to call and report the crime to begin with.

"I don't see how being a witness to a murder is dragging our name through the mud, Mother."

Regina looked at her only child in horrified disbelief. How could she have given birth to someone so addle-brained? So thick? "Have you lost all your sensibilities?" Wasn't it bad enough that her daughter had to play shopkeeper? Did she have to get mixed up with criminals, as well? "Has sinking down to the common world robbed you of your mind, Caitlin?"

Her mother's snobbery never failed to amaze her or leave a bitter taste in her mouth. "I don't call this sinking."

Regina tossed her head. Her earrings caught the fluorescent light and flashed it across the room. "Well, I do."

There would never be any common ground between them, Caitlin thought sadly. "That's your problem."

No, her problem was a bullheaded daughter who was bent on embarrassing her. "If you had given up this silly venture the way I advised you to, you wouldn't have been hopscotching through the alley at an ungodly hour to begin with. Then you wouldn't have seen anything."

Caitlin bit her lip, stifling a sigh. There was no point in arguing, in saying that she liked the life she led far more than her mother's. There were no words available in the English language that would convince Regina Cassidy of that.

"All water under the bridge, Mother. I did hopscotch and I did see." She glanced at the offending article. "And some idiot did write about it."

Thin fingers opened and closed impotently at Regina's side. "Other people will read this."

Caitlin turned away and busied herself with the display Kerry had abandoned. "I suspect if they pay for the newspaper, they might." She purposely kept her tone mild, refusing to be baited into an argument.

What went through that empty head of hers? "How am I to hold up my head when my daughter is involved in something so vulgar?" she demanded.

You, always you, Mother. Never me. Never a care about what might happen to me. "You'll find a way, Mother—you always have."

Rage clawed at Regina. Gripping her daughter's shoulder, she forced Caitlin to turn and face her. "You know, ever since that—that *savage* was in your life—"

Anger entered Caitlin's eyes. Gray might have walked out on her, but that didn't change the way she had once felt about him. And it didn't mean that her mother could rob him of his due.

"He's a Native American, Mother," she corrected tersely.

A mirthless smile twisted the genteel features. This, at least, had gone her way. "I don't care what he calls himself. He would have dragged you down even farther than this incident might—"

"Hello, Ms. Cassidy. Still espousing the same philosophies, I see."

Regina turned, paling slightly beneath her translucent makeup. They had been so involved arguing, neither woman had heard the bell ringing.

Graham Redhawk stood in the doorway. Regina stared at him as if she were watching an apparition.

"You," she whispered hoarsely, like Faustus greeting the devil at midnight.

Graham inclined his head in acknowledgment.

Regina swung around and glared at her daughter. "What, is he the other drug pusher?"

"No." Graham's voice was calm as he crossed to the women. "I'm investigating the *death* of the drug pusher."

Regina appeared as if she couldn't assimilate the information she'd just been given. "He's with the police department, Mother," Caitlin clarified.

Regina's thin nostrils flared slightly, as if she were standing downwind of something odious and very ripe. "A patrolman?" Crooked, no doubt. His kind always was.

"Detective," he corrected mildly.

Caitlin couldn't help seeing the humor in the situation. The list of people her mother looked down her nose at was extensive. Yet, under the right circumstances, she hypocritically denied it. Regina Cassidy had chaired at least one police charity. "You know, Mother, one of those people dedicated to protecting us."

Only one thing registered clearly. He was standing here, across from her daughter. Just the way he had eleven years ago. It was the ultimate insult.

"When did you start seeing him again?" Regina demanded, addressing her daughter as if Graham wasn't standing in the room.

"She didn't," he interjected coolly. "I've been assigned to her case, Mrs. Cassidy." He saw the surprised look on Caitlin's face.

That makes two of us, he thought.

Caitlin's mother looked as if she was going to curse him

and every single one of his ancestors, back to the dawn of time.

He wasn't wrong. "Is that the excuse you're using to crawl back into her life?"

Caitlin had had enough. She rounded the counter, placing herself between her mother and Graham. "Mother, if you're not going to buy anything, I'm afraid I'm going to have to ask you to leave. I don't have time to socialize." She thrust the newspaper back toward her mother.

Regina drew herself up, Marie Antoinette facing down the masses who were begging for sustenance. She had come with the sole intent of getting her daughter to give up this foolishness of pretending to run a business. "Are you coming with me?"

A stubborn glint entered Caitlin's eyes, one that Graham found very appealing despite himself. So, she had been serious when she had said that her mother no longer ran her life.

"I'm working, Mother."

Regina frosted everything in the path of her glance as she turned and walked to the door.

"Nice seeing you, too, Mother," Caitlin called out to the retreating back. The door slammed. The bell rang shrilly.

Graham's mouth curved. "She hasn't changed any."

"No," Caitlin agreed quietly, shaking her head. "No, she hasn't." Coming to life, she realized that the display her mother had scattered was still on the floor. She stooped to pick them up.

After a beat, Graham joined her. Awkwardly he picked up one pair of panties.

Despite the anger, the turmoil raging within her, Caitlin laughed. Gray looked so very uncomfortable, so out of place holding scraps of silk and lace in his large hands.

"Here." She took the red panties from him. "Before you turn completely beet-red."

He surrendered the article willingly. "I wasn't turning beet-red. Besides, according to your mother, that would be impossible to detect."

Caitlin sobered. "I'm sorry you had to hear that. She's still a bigot. If it makes you feel any better, you're on a long list of people she dislikes.''

He rose and watched her as she gathered the rest of the panties to her. ''Her feelings don't concern me. There are a lot of people like her around on both sides of the reservation.''

She stood, holding the undergarments against her. ''What are you doing here, anyway?'' The reason suddenly occurred to her. ''Did you catch him?''

''No.''

She didn't understand. She had told him everything she could think of. ''Then—?''

''I've been assigned to be your bodyguard.''

The panties she had just gathered fell from her hands to the floor.

Chapter 5

Caitlin stared at Graham, dumbfounded. "You're what?"

He didn't like this any more than she apparently did. He would rather have been anywhere in the world instead of here. But here was where he was supposed to be, and he was too much of a professional to let his feelings interfere with his work.

"I've been assigned to be your bodyguard."

The hell he had. For the second time she bent and scooped up the fallen underwear. She deposited the garments on the counter and raised her chin pugnaciously.

"No, you haven't."

He raised a brow at the challenge in her eyes. "Want to call the captain?"

"The marines if I have to," she countered. Anything to insure that he was not going to be here with her any longer than was absolutely necessary. She didn't want to have old feelings stirred up.

Now that her mother was no longer there to silently unite them by giving them a common enemy, they divided, returning to their respective corners, eyeing each other warily.

Scars from the past and the feeling of betrayal shimmered between them, an unspoken presence. An uninvited guest, pushing them apart.

Caitlin shook her head. "You can't stay here, hovering over me." She just wouldn't allow it. It was bad for business. How would it look, having a policeman loitering around?

Graham banked down the anger that flashed, red-hot, within him. "Believe me, it's not by choice."

He paused, debating. It was best to say nothing, to be like his mother, who restrained her words and doled them out sparingly. But there were other emotions bouncing around within him, emotions that wouldn't allow Graham to completely hold his tongue.

"You know, you're not really that different from your mother." He hadn't wanted to believe it last time. He didn't want to believe it now. But what else could he think? The evidence was staring him in the face.

Her mother was the last person Caitlin wanted to be compared to. Her eyes narrowed. "And what's that supposed to mean?"

She couldn't play innocent with him. He knew better, had been shown better. When it came down to it, she was just as bigoted as her mother. He wasn't about to play word games. "I think you know."

What was he talking about? She was the one who had been wronged, not him. "I wouldn't go throwing stones if I were you, Gray. You're not exactly an innocent here."

But he had been. Innocent, naive or maybe just plain stupid to believe that she would actually have married him. But she had to be referring to something else. "What are you talking about?"

If he thought she was going to let him see how much he had hurt her by taking her mother's money, by asking to be paid off, he was wrong. She'd die first. Caitlin looked longingly toward the door, wishing for a customer to take her attention away. But none came.

Par for the course. Nothing was going right today.

"You figure it out." She turned her back on him, arranging

the underwear in layers of three on the counter. "And while you're figuring it out, do it somewhere else, Gray. I won't have you in my store, scaring away customers."

Graham drew himself up. "I haven't burned a covered wagon or scalped anyone in at least a month."

She turned to look at him, her fingers wrapped around a small scrap of powder blue nylon that some designer envisioned as proper cover.

He couldn't mean—

Caitlin saw his expression and knew that he did. She was appalled, horrified and angry at the same time. How could he think so little of her?

"You think this is about—?" She couldn't bring herself to finish the sentence. He thought she was prejudiced, that it actually mattered to her that he was part Navajo. Dear God, she thought he knew her. Had she really loved this man as fiercely as she had and still remained a stranger to him?

Obviously she must have. He didn't know her at all.

Caitlin refrained from hitting his broad chest with the flat of her hand, though she wanted to. Badly. Maybe then she'd feel better.

"You jerk, this has nothing to do with covered wagons, burning or otherwise. Women don't like a man hanging around when they're debating buying lingerie for themselves. They think they're being measured up." Her eyes narrowed as she looked at his face. He was looking at the panties in her hand and she could almost read his thoughts. She tossed them aside. "Or undressed."

Caitlin moved behind the counter, wanting distance between them. Miles. The counter would have to do.

"I have a business to run. Now go and guard someone else's body." She pointed to the door that stubbornly remained unopened. "Or go write someone up for speeding."

He could see her wearing something like that. Soft and silky against her skin. Damn, what was the matter with him? Why was he torturing himself like this?

Clearing his mind, he raised his eyes to her face, his expression unreadable. "I don't write tickets."

"Good for you." Caitlin fairly spat it out.

Whether she liked it or not, she was in danger. And also whether she liked it or not, it was his job to protect her. He indicated the paper with his eyes. There was no point in pulling punches.

"Caitlin, that article your mother waved around told the killer that there was a witness to the crime. It told him who the witness was. You want to end up another statistic?"

She hated the frightened feeling that rose up to choke her. Hated feeling vulnerable. Because there was no one else to take it out on, he was her target. "You told me he was probably on a bus out of Phoenix."

He had said it because she'd been frightened. And because, at the time, there might have been a small chance that it was true. His eyes held hers. He tried not to remember how they used to mesmerize him. "I told you a lot of things you didn't believe."

Damn, she had cried Gray out of her system a long time ago. There were no tears left. So why did she feel this insistent press behind her eyes?

"No, I did believe you," she said quietly. "That was the problem."

He looked at her, waiting for an explanation. Waiting for something he could work with. Something that he could believe. But it was too late for that, he reminded himself. Years too late.

He had changed. His edges were sharper, harder. He wasn't that young boy on the brink of manhood anymore. He had lost the ability to believe in miracles. Having her and making a marriage work came under that heading. Miracles.

Caitlin squared her shoulders. "Look, I meant what I said. You can't stay here."

It was almost a plea, though her voice remained emotionless. It wasn't only the customers she didn't want him interfering with. It was her. Her mind, her life. Having him around was just too painful to endure.

If she had told herself she was over him—over the heartache—seeing him here, looking more hauntingly handsome than ever, told her that she had only been lying to herself. She wasn't over him at all. But he didn't have to know that.

He remained where he was, a solid, steadfast tin soldier. Tiny sparks of desperation began to shoot through her. "Can't you watch me from across the street? Canvass the area? Something?"

It could be done. Not comfortably, but then, he hadn't joined the force to be comfortable. "Is it that hard for you to look at me?"

There was no hesitation. "Yes."

He had his answer. No matter what she feigned to the contrary, how tolerant she pretended to be, it was obvious that Caitlin still felt the same way she had when she had written that letter to him. The letter that told him she had changed her mind about marrying him. That a marriage between them would be a mistake that they would both regret in time. The letter that ended his only dream.

In his heart he had always known that it wouldn't work out between them. That what they had was too fragile, too precious to survive. But stubbornly he had tried, ignoring warnings, ignoring the odds. Reading the words, seeing them in black and white, had cut him to the bone.

And ripped out the heart that had been hers.

Maybe he'd be better off outside at that. At any rate, for all intents and purposes, he already was.

Graham nodded shortly. "All right, have it your way."

Caitlin watched him leave without another word. She stood very still as the sound of the bell faded into the air. For a moment she couldn't move. She felt drained.

"If I had," she whispered to the man who was no longer there, "things would have been very different."

The rustling curtain behind her startled Caitlin. She turned in surprise. She'd forgotten that she wasn't alone.

"Is it safe to come out yet?" Sticking out her curly blond head, Kerry peered through the parted curtains. Eva gave Caitlin a shy look and returned to her work as if nothing had happened. Eva liked minding her own business. No such affliction plagued Kerry.

Caitlin laughed. Thank God for Kerry. Thank God for someone she could talk to about absolutely nothing. "Come on out, you coward."

Kerry saw no purpose in denying what was true. She had no desire to get into an argument with Caitlin's mother or the big, strong, silent police detective. There were better things to do with men like that, anyway.

She pulled the curtain closed behind her. "What's the body count?"

Caitlin gestured around the store. There were no customers. She hoped the newspaper story hadn't chased them away. That would really be adding insult to injury.

"None."

Kerry looked wistfully toward the door. "I see the hunk left."

Caitlin's mouth curved. For Kerry, men fell into only two categories: hunks and nonhunks. "Yes."

Kerry began to languidly straighten out a display that was in perfect order. Her mind wasn't on her work. "I couldn't help overhearing…"

Caitlin had edged over to the far side of the counter. From there she could just make out Graham's retreating back. He was getting into a navy blue sedan. She wondered if the pink Caddie was parked at the precinct.

"Kerry, 'overhearing' is a hobby with you." Besides, they had been almost shouting. Overhearing wouldn't have been a difficult matter.

Kerry grinned. "Guilty as charged. You know him, huh?"

Caitlin sighed involuntarily. It sounded too soulful for her own liking. She tried to look indifferent. "Yes, I know him."

Unlike Caitlin, Kerry made no attempt to disguise her interest in Graham's movements. She crossed to the window to see where he was. Spotting him, she glanced over her shoulder at Caitlin. "Thinking of picking up where you left off with him?"

The smile left Caitlin's face as if a giant eraser had wiped it away with a single pass. "No."

Kerry's interest rose another notch. "Then can I have him?"

Caitlin shook her head. Kerry had no idea what she would be getting herself into. A man who would break her heart with no compunction if the price was right. "Kerry, call the shipping company and find out where the last order went. It was supposed to be here yesterday."

Kerry saluted after giving Graham one last, longing look. Her eyes shifted to her friend. "If it were me, I wouldn't leave him sitting out there like that where any woman could get at him."

Any woman who got to Graham Redhawk deserved him. Besides, the man was married. Remembering that irritated her further, though she knew she was being contradictory. "Well, you're not me."

Kerry shrugged philosophically. "I know. More's the pity."

Caitlin looked at Kerry pointedly. "The shipment?"

Kerry turned, on her way to the back room and the telephone. "I hear and obey."

By her own count, Caitlin knew she had to have walked past the front window a dozen times, on one pretext or another. Each time she did, she looked out. And each time she saw Graham still sitting in the car. Just as he had been for the past two hours.

He looked resigned, bored and stoic. And probably damn hot.

Guilt ate away at her.

It had to be a hundred degrees outside. They hadn't hit anything under a hundred for the past seven days in a row. The car was parked in minimal shade and the windows were open, but he had to be unbearably hot and uncomfortable.

Kerry passed by with the first armload of negligees from the wayward shipment, which had finally arrived less than half an hour ago. She stopped to peer over Caitlin's shoulder.

"How long do you think he'll have to stay in there before he's well-done?"

Caitlin turned away, taking the armload of delicate negligees from her. She was going to hang them around the antique armoire.

"Well-done?" she repeated innocently.

Caitlin wasn't fooling her. She had seen her friend wander over to the window and look out more than once. "Done. You know, two hundred degrees for two hours." A smile tugged at her mouth, though she tried to keep a straight face. "Isn't that long enough to roast a hunk of beef?"

As if Graham needed a champion. Caitlin took a pink satin hanger from the armoire and placed the first negligee on it. "In the first place, it's not two hundred degrees out there—"

Logic was expendable. "Must feel like it after a while."

Caitlin reached for a second hanger, selecting a different color. "And he's not a hunk of beef."

Kerry's sigh bordered on primal. "No? Then what is he?"

The response was automatic. "A jerk."

Sometime, when they were alone over a couple of cartons of ice cream, she meant to ply Caitlin with questions. But now wasn't the time.

"Doesn't look like a jerk to me." Kerry peered out the window again just as a customer entered. She smiled at the woman automatically. "But he does look hot," she told Caitlin, lowering her voice. "In every sense of the word." A wistful sigh ended the sentence. She crossed to Caitlin and cocked her head, studying her. "You know, I'd be feeling pretty guilty by now."

A petite blonde approached Caitlin. She held a hot-pink thong bikini in her hand. "Where can I try this on?"

The cavalry to the rescue. Caitlin turned and all but pushed Kerry toward the woman. "Kerry will take you to the dressing room."

Kerry gave her a knowing look that promised further discussion at the first opportunity. Kerry wouldn't be satisfied until she had the complete story, spread out before her like a miniseries, Caitlin thought.

She wasn't going to be up to that any time soon, she thought. Maybe after this whole episode was over…

The telephone rang, cutting her thoughts short. She picked up the receiver on the third ring. "Naughty But Nice," Caitlin recited automatically. "How may I help you?"

There was an awkward pause on the other end of the line. "What sort of place is this?" a woman's voice finally asked.

It was obviously a wrong number, Caitlin thought. The name of her store was whimsical. The innuendo tended to throw some people off. She smiled to herself as she cradled the telephone against her shoulder. "It's a lingerie store."

"Oh." There was another long pause. Caitlin was about to hang up when the woman asked, "Is Graham Redhawk there, by any chance?"

Caitlin stiffened. It was his wife. His wife was calling him here. She knew it as certainly as if the woman had introduced herself. Caitlin's fingers felt suddenly cold as she took the receiver into her hand.

"Just a minute, I'll get him for you." She didn't remember placing the telephone down on the desk a moment after she did it.

Caitlin nodded at a customer just entering the store, feeling oddly hollow as she walked out. The hot air hit her like heat coming from an open oven. It made breathing difficult. There was no other reason for the oppressive feeling crawling through her veins.

She crossed the newly repaved street. They had taken the sawhorses away just this morning. If the work had been finished two days earlier, Caitlin thought bitterly, she wouldn't be going through this.

Graham watched her approach, attempting to read the look on her face. He wasn't successful. There hadn't been anyone suspicious-looking entering the store. He'd been out of the car during the delivery, making his presence known to the delivery man. The stocky man had unloaded the cartons and left without incident.

Other than that, for the past two hours, traffic in and out of the store had been minimal.

What was she doing out here? She had acted as if she never wanted to see him again. There was an oddly hollow look in her eyes. He opened the door and got out. "Anything wrong?"

"There's someone on the phone for you. I think it might be your wife." The words felt as if they weighed ten pounds apiece.

Graham immediately crossed the street. It was as if he'd been waiting for the call, she thought.

Can't wait to talk to her, can you? A stab of completely unwarranted pain went through her.

Caitlin shook her head as if to clear it and followed him into the store, telling herself that it no longer mattered to her whom he talked to.

"You can take it in the back." She gestured toward the room. He hardly nodded as he strode across the floor and disappeared behind the curtain.

The display by the armoire was waiting. Caitlin dawdled, moving toward the rear by the teddy display. She found herself straining to listen, even though his voice was low.

What was Celia doing, calling him? Graham wondered. He had expected the lawyer to return his call, not her.

He supposed that it was just as well. He wasn't very good with go-betweens. Maybe they could still settle this between them, without hurting Jake. That was all that really mattered.

Graham jerked the receiver up. "Redhawk."

"Police work has gotten nicer, I see." Celia's soft, low voice filled his ear. "What are you doing hanging around a lingerie shop?"

Though sublimated, that old, familiar jealous tone was there. Celia had always been resentful of his work. "Guarding a witness."

"Well, I hope you enjoy yourself." Bitterness entered on the next wave. It didn't take long, Graham thought. "Your work always did come first."

His hand tightened slightly on the receiver. Here it came.

"Not before Jake," he said honestly. He wasn't about to lie to her. That wasn't the way he was going to keep Jake, telling her lies. While he had cared about Celia, he had never loved her, never told her that he did. In the beginning, she'd been a warm body to soothe his troubled soul. In time, even the caring had dissolved.

Celia took the opening. "About Jake—"

Yes, about Jake. "You can't have him," he said flatly. "End of discussion."

Celia didn't see it that way. "Things have changed for me, Graham. I know I went through a rootless period, but I know who I am now."

She had abandoned a small boy, hurt him without giving it a single thought while she went on a quest to find her inner self. It was a bunch of garbage.

"I'm glad for you," he said coolly, "but you still can't have him."

A wave of anxiety entered her voice. Her words rushed at him, assaulting his ear. "I'm married again, Gray. I'm Mrs. Shephard now. Rob is a wonderful man. Rich, too."

Graham knew how much money meant to her. Celia had always thrown their financial situation in his face, angry that she was denied the finer things in life because he refused to leave himself open to bribes. Because he took pride in being an honest cop.

She had chafed that there was never extra money for vacations or to buy the larger house she had set her heart on.

In the end, she had walked out over that as much as anything. She wanted something else, something better, she had said. That didn't include him, or their son.

"That must make you very happy," he said dryly.

"It would, if I had Jake."

She was in a maternal mode again. The last time it had lasted all of a year, until the adoption had been finalized. Then, inexplicably, Celia seemed to lose interest in Jake. Graham had taken over grudgingly, doing for the boy. The love that had always eluded him he found mirrored in the boy's deep brown eyes. He wasn't about to give that up.

"That didn't seem to be on your mind when you left."

Celia knew she had made mistakes and was willing to admit to them. But not be stopped by them. "I was confused. I didn't know what I wanted."

"And now you do." There was no mistaking the sarcasm in his voice. "Enjoy what you have, Celia. Leave us alone."

"I want Jake," she cried stubbornly, her voice rising in the phone.

He had been taken in once, when she had pleaded and begged him to agree to the adoption. He knew better than to go down that same path again. "So you can play mother until you get tired of it again?"

"It's not like that anymore. I can give him things, things you can't. A good education, a stable life. A place in the community." The last had been a dig and they both knew it.

He wasn't going to let her bait him. His temper was a fearsome thing when he lost it and he wasn't about to give her the satisfaction of goading him. "He has a place in the community. As my son."

Her voice rose, growing more reedy. "You know I can't have any more children."

If he had had any compassion for her, it had died a long time ago—when he had found Jake crying because Celia had left him.

"Adopt. You did it before."

His cold tone enraged her. "I'll see you in court if I have to."

As soon as he had heard her voice, Graham had known it would come down to this. Celia indulged in theatrics when it suited her. She probably even believed that she wanted Jake back. For now. "Then I guess you'll just have to."

He hung up before she could raise her voice again. Discussions with Celia in the last years of their marriage always ended on the same note. She would scream at him and he would become silent, walking away. There was no purpose in arguing. Celia never came around to see his side in anything.

Graham strode out from behind the curtain. Caitlin wasn't more than two feet away. Their eyes met. She didn't bother pretending that she was busy arranging a display.

"Trouble at home?"

He lifted a shoulder and let it fall. "In a manner of speaking."

He didn't feel like going into it. If Caitlin hadn't run away when she had, he would never have met Celia. But then, he would never have had Jake in his life, either, so he supposed it evened out.

There was distress in his eyes. She saw it a moment before he blanketed it. Compassion stirred almost against her will. "Want to talk about it?"

His expression hardened. He didn't need her pity. "No."

She sighed. Why had she even bothered? "Same old Gray."

His eyes held hers for a minute. "It doesn't concern you."

Once, everything about him had concerned her. But then he had thrown all that away. "You're right, it doesn't." The sudden wave of anger subsided as she saw him walking toward the front door again. She bit her lip, debating.

"It's hot outside," she began.

He had his hand on the door. "It's always hot outside."

As if an unseen hand was pushing her, Caitlin slowly crossed over to him. She could see a slight bead of perspiration along his forehead. The guilt increased. "You're sweating."

The expression on his face strove for uninterest. "Even Native Americans sweat."

She was about to snap at him that he was being a bigger fathead than usual, then stopped. It sounded as if he had just gone through a great deal on the phone. But that still didn't give him the right to talk to her as if she were a copy of her mother.

Abruptly she cleared off a space on the counter. "Here."

He looked down at it. What was she showing him? There was nothing there. "What?"

"Anytime you want to take that rather conspicuous chip off your shoulder, you can park it right here. In the meantime, you can stay in the shop. I don't want your burned carcass on my conscience."

His lips curved, but the smile didn't reach his eyes. They remained flat. "I'm surprised you have room in your conscience for anything else."

That did it. He was hopeless. Stifling an oath only because there was a customer in the store, Caitlin grabbed her purse from under the counter and headed for the door. "I'm going out to lunch, Kerry," she called over her shoulder.

It was past two. She had intended to work through lunch and have some take-out food delivered, but this was too much to put up with. She needed some air, even if it was hot.

"Not without me, you're not." Gray was directly behind her, shadowing her steps to the door.

"Terrific." She ground out the word through her teeth.

Chapter 6

Graham reached over and pushed open the door for her, letting her walk out first. "So, where do you usually eat?"

"Usually? Out of a paper bag in the back room." She nodded toward the store. Her eyes met his. "But I suddenly need some space." She'd wanted to get away from him, but that obviously wasn't about to happen.

Caitlin looked up and down the street. She had never really noticed how many people there were out here. So many different faces.

What if one of them—?

She couldn't shake away the fear. It surrounded her with a vise-like grip. "Do you really think he's out there?"

Caitlin spoke softly, attempting to hide the anxiety she felt. But he detected a hitch in her voice. He was tempted to contradict himself. Even so, he couldn't lie to her.

"Yeah, I do." He began to guide her across the street. "The captain wouldn't have assigned me to you if there wasn't that chance."

Her mouth felt dry. Caitlin nodded in agreement, hardly aware that she was following him. This was a nightmare. How could her life be turned upside down so easily, so quickly? The police didn't do things on a whim. They believed that she was a potential target.

Digging deep, Caitlin tried to make light of the situation. She didn't quite carry it off. "So how long are you going to hang around like this?"

The light turned red at the corner, forcing them to wait.

"Tentatively, two weeks." That was how long the captain projected. Graham knew it would become a private matter for him if the killer hadn't been located by then. "With luck, the leads we have might get us somewhere by then."

She heard the skepticism in his voice. "But you don't think so."

The light turned green and he stepped off the curb. Graham scanned the immediate area as he walked. It was second nature to him. "I don't believe much in luck."

She glanced at him and remembered the way Gray had looked when he had proposed to her. He'd sounded so sure of himself, so sure of their future. "You did once."

His mouth hardened a little. "Yeah, and I learned from that experience." He ushered her toward his car. "Where do you want to go?"

Somewhere far away. From everything. She banked down her fears as well as the other emotions swirling within her. Reason set in. Caitlin glanced over her shoulder toward the store. That was reality, she thought. That was her anchor.

"Somewhere quick. I have to get back to work. Kerry doesn't like handling everything by herself and Eva works only half days."

Caitlin began to walk toward her own car. It was parked in the lot directly behind his. Graham remained where he was. He saw no reason to take hers when his was close. "Why don't we take my car?"

"I like mine." If she had to go with him, she wanted to drive. It relaxed her to drive and she desperately wanted to relax, to ease this tension away and pretend that everything was still all right. "I enjoy driving."

Graham shrugged. If it made her happy. "Have it your

way.'' As they approached her car he stopped in front of it. ''Pop the hood.''

Caitlin tapped her code out on the car's keypad and the locks snapped open on all four doors. She looked at him, puzzled. ''Why?''

There were too many horror stories for him to recount. He didn't want to frighten her any more than was absolutely necessary. ''I like being thorough. It makes me breathe easier at night.''

Shrugging, she leaned in and pulled the hood release. When the hood popped up, she walked around to the front of the small car and looked down at the mass of hoses, belts and gears. What was he looking for?

''Afraid the engine won't start?'' Caitlin asked whimsically.

Nothing looked out of order. No colorful wires, no surprises. ''Checking for explosives.''

''Explosives?'' That brought to mind organized crime. Professionals. The color drained from her face as she stared at Graham. ''Just who was it that you think I saw kill that man?''

For a moment he thought of protecting her. But she might as well know all of it. She had the right. Besides, it would keep her from taking foolish chances.

''The dead man was connected to a drug cartel. As a rule, they don't like leaving loose ends.'' He slammed the hood shut. ''That includes witnesses. But it doesn't look as if they've planted anything in your car.''

Oh, God, what had she walked into? ''You're not kidding, are you?''

Her eyes pleaded with him to say that he was. Graham shook his head and then checked under the car.

Her palms were damp and the air in her lungs felt like a hardening, leaden weight. She looked at the dark sedan on the street. ''We'll take your car.''

''Good choice.''

She hit the security lock and all four locks snapped down. A tiny light on the dashboard turned on, assuring her the alarm was engaged. The fact hardly registered. "You're not doing this just to scare me, are you?"

He led the way to his car, shortening his stride to stay abreast of her. "I don't play games, Caitlin."

No, he never had. Not until the end. And then he had gone for high stakes.

Unlocking the car, Graham held the door open for her. She glanced at the exterior as she got in. "What happened to the Caddie?"

"As you mentioned, it tends to stand out. Right now, I'm more interested in blending in." Graham watched her slide in on the passenger side, then closed the door. Rounding the trunk, he got in on the driver's side. "Where to?" he asked again.

She struggled to pull her thoughts together. She wasn't going to be any good to herself if she came unraveled. This would be over soon enough. It just had to be.

"Caitlin?"

Belatedly she realized that he was talking to her. "What?"

"Where do you want to go for lunch?" he repeated patiently.

She licked her lips and blew out a long breath. *Relax,* she ordered herself.

"Stop at the fast-food place at the end of the next block. Monty's."

"Monty's?"

Caitlin had said she wanted somewhere quick, but he would have thought that she'd go for something a little more sophisticated than a fast-food restaurant. He pictured her in high-class establishments with meals that were aesthetically arranged on the plate by a fussy chef and that took a substantial bite out of a man's wallet if he was part of the working class.

It matched the image of the woman he thought she had become.

He sounded surprised, Caitlin thought. Had he forgotten all the times they had gone to the drive-through when they were going together? He hadn't had the money to pay for anything more expensive and she hadn't wanted to embarrass him, so, rather than hurt his pride, she'd professed a preference for hamburgers that sat waiting in paper wrappers beneath bulbs. In time, she had grown to like them.

A smile curved her mouth of its own accord. "Someone once got me hooked on junk food." Her shoulders moved slightly beneath her aqua blouse in a half shrug. "I never got over it."

He was trying vainly not to allow her smile to dislodge memories that were sealed away in strongboxes behind brick walls. He guided the car away from the curb. "Junk food it is."

Caitlin attempted to relax in her seat, but couldn't. Every bone in her body was rigid. Someone out there could be stalking her at this very moment. To add to that, here she was, just where she didn't want to be, next to Gray in a small space.

Isolated from the world.

Waves of old feelings ran fingers over her insistently like a child reaching out, trying to get her attention.

She'd been a child herself back then, she reminded herself. A child led by her emotions. She wasn't a child anymore. She could get through this.

In any event, she sincerely doubted it could get any worse.

The lot behind Monty's was fairly full. Graham frowned. He would have chosen a far less trafficked place. But if coming here made her feel better, maybe it was worth it.

Pulling up into a space, he stopped the car and got out. She didn't wait for him to open her door. She liked being her own woman, he thought. Good. She might look fragile, but she would get through this.

Graham opened one of the four doors leading into the restaurant and held it for her. Before she could enter, a crowd of teenagers pushed their way through, laughing, oblivious to the fact that they had nudged her out of the way.

He took her arm. "Sure you don't want to go somewhere else?"

She shook her head. Suddenly she wanted very much to be

here, where she had gone countless times before. She needed to have something familiar, to follow a normal pattern and forget the craziness that hovered just outside her. "I'm sure."

Graham shrugged and ushered her in. He was probably being overprotective, he thought.

They wove their way beyond the booths to the front counter. Despite the fact that it was past lunch hour, the restaurant was crowded, and getting more so. He looked around. The walls were littered with framed movie stills dating back to the forties. The booths were circa that era. The entire restaurant had a Hollywood flavor about it. She probably loved it here, he thought. He remembered her affinity for old movies.

Maybe the noise and familiar decor would change how she was feeling, she thought—scared and shaky and so damn exposed. She glanced over her shoulder at Graham. She felt exposed in more ways than one.

Turning, she stepped out of line. "Why don't you get me a large cheeseburger, fries and a soda?"

He grabbed her arm before she could leave. "Where are you going?"

Very carefully she extricated her arm. She didn't want him touching her. No matter what she told herself to the contrary, his touch unleashed things within her, things that were better left alone.

"To the ladies' room to throw some water on my face." She read his mind. "It's in the back and you can't come with me, Gray."

Graham nodded, but he wasn't happy about it. "Why didn't you go before we left?"

The question made her laugh and eased a little of the tension shooting through her shoulders. "You're beginning to sound like a father." Her smile widened at his glare. "Line's moving," she observed.

He moved forward, looking at her grudgingly.

"I want large fries," Caitlin added as she hurried away.

She just needed a few minutes to pull herself together, Caitlin thought. Just a few minutes to herself and she'd be fine.

That was all she had wanted to begin with, before Graham had strong-armed his way into accompanying her.

The bathroom was in the rear of the restaurant. She allowed herself to absorb the atmosphere as she went.

Pushing open a swinging door marked Rest Rooms, Caitlin walked into a narrow corridor that was located just behind the kitchen. While the dining area had a festive motif, the bright atmosphere ended abruptly beyond the door. The corridor leading to the rest room was dim and stark, not unlike other rest-room areas in small restaurants built for high traffic rather than for high quality.

She hesitated, looking around. It was dark in here.

Get hold of yourself, Cait.

Graham was just exaggerating, she told herself. Maybe this was his way of getting back at her. She couldn't continue behaving like a frightened child. Life went on.

She reached out to push the swinging bathroom door open. A hand darted out from behind her, grabbing her wrist just before she made contact with the surface.

Her heart caught in her throat, hammering wildly. Her purse fell from her other hand.

"Don't turn around," a low voice growled in her ear. The man was behind her, closer than a shadow. "Just walk to the side."

She'd seen a flash of gray material, the sleeve of a suit, when he'd grabbed her wrist. The smell of perspiration was heavy in the air. His? Her own? She fought to keep her head from whirling.

"Who are you?" She knew, though the question came automatically. If she kept him talking here, maybe Graham would—

The man pushed her head against the doorjamb as she tried to turn around. She swallowed a gasp of surprise and pain.

"Don't look, just follow orders. There's an exit right here. We're going to use it." Wrenching her arm up behind her until she thought it would snap, he yanked her to the side.

The restaurant continued filling up. There were too many people here. Maybe Graham was being paranoid, but it was making him very uneasy.

It kept nibbling at him. He shouldn't have let her go off by herself.

The gangly teenager behind the counter took the ten from him and began making change. Graham had no intention of taking the tray and looking for a table. He wanted to get Caitlin first.

"Watch this for me." Graham didn't bother looking at the boy. "I'll be right back."

"Sir, you can't leave your food here!" the boy called after him.

Graham ignored him. Weaving his way through a gaggle of children all dressed in the same bright green summer-camp T-shirt, he made his way to the rear of the restaurant.

Something didn't feel right.

He couldn't put his finger on it. But there was enough of his mother in him for Graham to have a healthy respect for premonitions.

The tables in the rear were nearly all occupied with teen-agers, businessmen out for a late, quick bite and mothers with small children in tow.

Caitlin wasn't anywhere to be seen.

How long did it take to throw water on your face?

Just before he entered the corridor, the sound of a door closing caught his attention. But no one was in the corridor. He thought of entering the women's bathroom when he saw her purse on the floor.

Damn!

A beam of daylight was shining through the crack where the side door didn't quite meet the jamb. Adrenaline went into overdrive.

Graham yanked open the door. Someone in a light gray suit was just disappearing around the corner in the alleyway. Monty's was buttressed against an industrial complex that ran the length of the block on the other side. No one in a suit had any business being back here.

Swearing viciously at himself for letting Caitlin out of his sight, Graham covered the butt of his gun with his hand. Pulling it free of its holster, Graham sprinted after the man.

As he raced around the corner, he saw that the man was shoving Caitlin toward a car parked just at the mouth of the alley. Pouring on speed, he cut the distance between them.

The man jerked around just as Graham called out his warning.

"Freeze!" He stopped, taking aim. "This is the police."

It happened too quickly for Graham to react. The man threw Caitlin at him and bolted into his car. Graham's gun went flying as Caitlin collided with him. He was thrown to the ground, hitting the back of his head on the cement as Caitlin landed on top of him.

The tires screeched as the car roared into life and came straight at them.

Graham barely had time to roll out of the way, pulling Caitlin with him. They rolled into the side of a Dumpster.

Feeling dazed, Graham jumped to his feet, memorizing as much of the license plate number as he could see. It was probably a stolen vehicle, but there was always a chance that it might check out.

The car was gone in the next heartbeat. Graham looked down at Caitlin. She was struggling to her feet. He took her hand in his and helped her up. "Are you all right?"

She nodded numbly, her fingers curled about his. "You're right. I should have gone at the shop." And then her bravado vanished. She turned her face into his chest. "Oh, Gray..."

For a moment he just let her stand there, unable to leave the grip of frozen feelings, of what might have been. And then awkwardly he began to stroke her hair. "Yeah, I know."

Slowly they returned to him—all the old feelings. It was like riding a bicycle—once it was ingrained, you never forgot. His arms tightened around her. The stroking became less awkward as warmth and emotions unfurled.

Her tears were dampening his chest. Graham felt impotent anger rage within him against the man who had done this to her, who had threatened her and frightened her so badly.

Who might have killed her if he hadn't followed his instincts and gone looking for her.

Graham raised her chin and slowly wiped away her tears with his thumb.

"We'll get him, Caitlin. I swear I won't let him hurt you."

She knew he meant it. Caitlin nodded as she looked up at him, her eyes bright with tears she was fighting hard to keep from shedding.

He couldn't help himself. He didn't even know, when he thought of it later, if he even tried to stop what was happening. Graham lowered his mouth to hers and kissed her because there was absolutely nothing else he could do at the moment. It was as if he had read a page out of his destiny and that was what was written on it. At this moment he was to kiss her. Even if the world stopped.

And for that moment, it did.

Shaking, lost, in need of comfort, she let herself be drawn into the kiss. Fear, anxiety, confusion all melded, sublimating their identities into a whirlwind that seized her. It pulled her in as it swirled about, disorienting her.

The only focal point she had was his mouth. And she clung to it.

To him.

Her body pressed closer. Graham held her against him, forgetting the past, forgetting the pain, remembering only that once, she had made him feel like a young, bronzed god. Made him feel as if he could touch the sky as he walked the earth.

God, but he had missed her. He knew then that she had continued to haunt the shadows of his mind, like a whisper of what couldn't have been. And that, no matter what, she would always be there, a glimmer of what he could never have.

Surprised by the magnitude of emotion erupting between them, they pulled apart. Graham felt his blood racing through his veins, hot, demanding. His face gave no indication of what he was feeling. But for a fleeting moment, his eyes did.

And she saw.

He crossed to pick up the gun he had dropped. "Still hungry?'' His tone was casual, almost distant, as if a moment ago she hadn't felt like heaven in his arms.

Someone else's heaven, not his own.

She shook her head. Very slowly she dusted herself off. The tears threatened to come again, but she managed to hold them back. She suddenly felt very, very tired.

Graham looked at her. Her hands were still shaking. He could have killed that bastard. If only there had been a clear shot—

Swearing inwardly, Graham reined in his emotions. He couldn't afford to let them cloud his mind, interfering with what he was sworn to do. Uphold the law.

He holstered the gun and covered it with his jacket. ''Let me take you home, Caitlin.''

She was going to protest that she was fine, that she had to get back to the shop. But she wasn't fine. She was terrified. And very confused. About everything.

Caitlin dragged her hand through her hair, vainly seeking composure. How did someone act who was nearly kidnapped and then rescued and catapulted to the past in less than ten minutes? She hadn't a clue. ''Maybe you'd better.''

She really was afraid, he thought, his anger surging higher. If he'd been just a little faster, a second closer, he might have gotten that slime and ended this ordeal for her.

Graham looked down at her face. There was no stubborn glint in her eye, no challenge in her bearing. That lowlife had frightened her. Badly.

''C'mon.'' Graham took her arm and ushered her back through the exit she'd been forced through. She flinched involuntarily as she crossed the threshold into the restaurant.

Graham stooped to pick up her purse and handed it to her without a word. Taking her arm again, he guided her to the front.

She had to get hold of herself. The sight of mothers with their children, of the teenagers teasing one another, grounded her. She felt a little better.

''I can walk, Graham,'' she protested.

''I know.'' His hand remained where it was. He crossed to

the last line, where his tray still stood on the counter. Recognition flashed through the server's eyes as Graham approached. "We'll take that to go."

The teenager nodded so quickly the blue-and-red peaked paper cap fell off his head. He ignored it. Instead, he reached beneath the counter for a paper sack and hurriedly shoveled both orders into it. His hands seemed to get in his way as he rushed.

Despite everything, it made Caitlin smile. "You seem to have this overwhelming effect on people," she whispered into Graham's ear.

Her breath curled along his face, warm, sweet. Graham looked at Caitlin. *So do you, Caitlin. So do you.*

She insisted that they stop at the shop to tell Kerry what had happened. Caitlin was resigned to closing the shop for the day, but Kerry volunteered to remain until closing time and then close up herself.

"You just go home and rest," she ordered, concerned. By her expression, it was clear Kerry had no doubts that the detective would see that Caitlin stayed put.

As they drove to her house, Graham called in the incident on his radio, giving the dispatcher the license number. He'd managed to remember all but the last digit. The make and model of the car would make up for it. It had been a California plate.

Silence rode with them after he replaced the radio receiver. They both had things to think about. Too much was being stuffed into too small a space.

He had too much going on in his life already to have this happening, he thought. But it didn't change anything. His feelings were still there, as futile as ever. Except that this time, he *knew* how futile they were.

The address she had given him belonged to a modest one-story house, nestled on the outskirts of the city. He had pictured her living somewhere more opulent, expensive.

Wrong again.

It was a fairly new development. Her house was on a major through street, its back to a right-of-way. He didn't like it. It made her too accessible. Calling in again, he gave the address to the dispatcher and asked for a patrol car to be assigned to drive periodically through the area.

Graham pulled up in her driveway and turned off the engine. Another officer would bring her car home for her later. He made no move to get out. "Maybe you should stay at a hotel for the time being."

She'd had time to gather herself together on the ride home. Some of her spirit had returned. "He's not going to chase me out of my home, Gray."

He nodded, understanding her feelings. Having something to hang on to was important. It was one of the reasons his mother had gone back to the reservation after his father had deserted them. Roots.

Getting out of the car, he walked with Caitlin to the front door, quietly scanning the area as he did so. There was no one outside.

There was no keypad on the wall next to the door. Graham raised a brow as he glanced at her. "No security system?"

She shook her head. She hadn't really seen the need for one.

"You should have one installed." He held out his hand. "Give me your key."

Her fingers still felt clumsy as she hunted for the key. Finding it, she gave it to him, then shifted restlessly from foot to foot, looking around. Everything appeared to be just as it had been when she had left it this morning. But it wasn't. In the past few hours her feeling of being safe had been stolen away. And the sky had fallen on her.

She stared at Graham's back as he went to check out the rooms.

Yes, the sky had fallen. In more ways than one.

Chapter 7

Graham moved methodically from room to room, checking behind drapes, inside closets and along window frames. There was no sign of forced entry. Nothing had been tampered with. Satisfied, he returned to the living room.

Caitlin was still standing where he had left her, as if being there could somehow keep her safe.

He only hoped that *he* could do that for her. "No one's been here."

She shivered and ran her hands along her arms as she let out a long, shaky breath. "Do you think he'll try to break in?"

Graham didn't answer her question directly. He gave her the only assurance he could. "I'll be staying here with you."

It was a no-win situation. One threatened her life, the other her peace of mind. "For how long?"

He sat on the sofa. "For however long it takes."

Despite the past, she had to admit that having him here made her feel safer. But she also knew that this wasn't an indefinite situation. "Won't the police department have something to say about that?"

After today's attempt, he knew the two-week limit would be extended. "Things can be arranged." Graham glanced over his shoulder toward the rear of the house. "Would have made things more comfortable if you hadn't turned the spare bedroom into a den."

Caitlin laughed dryly, wishing the unsettling fluttering in her stomach would stop. "I wasn't expecting to be stalked."

He hated the sound of that. Hated the thought of what it did to her. She shouldn't have to be afraid like this. No one should. "Yeah, well, with any luck, that situation won't be for long."

She glanced toward the window. Had that car been parked there before?

Get a grip, Cait, that's only the new van of the woman across the street.

She turned toward Graham. "I thought you didn't believe in luck."

"I don't. But you do. That evens things out." Graham opened the paper sack he'd dropped on the coffee table and spread out the contents. There were two straws, but nothing to put them in. He raised his eyes to her face. "I forgot the sodas."

"I've got some in the refrigerator." Caitlin started to leave the room, then looked at the two mounds that represented their cheeseburgers and the limp fries peering out of the bright red containers. "You can eat that stuff cold?"

"Food's food." He unwrapped his cheeseburger, then set it down on the table. "I learned a long time ago not to be fussy."

She remembered what he had told her about his childhood. How his father had abandoned his mother, taking with him what little money they'd had. His mother had returned to the reservation in shame, bringing her young son with her. They had subsisted on the charity of her relatives and government handouts. It had been for only a short while, but it had left an indelible impression on him.

Caitlin returned with two small bottles of soda. She placed

one in front of Graham and held the other as she perched on the sofa next to him.

She looked like a sparrow about to take flight at the faintest sight of a hawk on the horizon. He wondered how much of that was due to the threat of the killer and how much was due to him.

Graham pushed her cheeseburger toward her. "Have some," he prodded. "It'll take your mind off what's going on."

That she sincerely doubted. There was too much going on for her mind to be distracted by food. Especially cold food. But she picked the cheeseburger up, mechanically unwrapping it. What appetite she had had was gone.

She looked at Graham. He was eating, looking as if he were unfazed by everything that had happened. If not for the tight line along his jaw and the way he had looked at her when he had helped her up in the alley, she would have been completely fooled.

He was good at that, keeping his emotions in check, not letting things get to him. Unlike her, she thought.

Two bites later Caitlin put the cheeseburger back down on its colorful wrapper. Graham stopped eating and raised a quizzical brow.

"I'm not hungry."

Caitlin let out another long, shaky breath as she looked around the room. This was her home, her haven when the world got a little too crazy. She was supposed to feel safe here.

Why didn't she?

Her eyes shifted to Graham. Tall, stoic, unflappable Gray.

"Talk to me, Gray. Talk to me so that I don't think about anything." She pushed the food away as she turned her face toward his. "Tell me about your son—"

She realized that she had forgotten the boy's name. Her head felt as if it had been entirely emptied of everything.

"Jake?" he supplied. Why did she want to know about him?

"Yes, Jake," she repeated. She wanted to hear about his

son. About something wonderfully normal. Without thinking, she placed her hand on his wrist. "Does he look like you?"

He thought for a second. Jake looked like Jake to him. "Yes, I suppose in an odd way, he does."

Caitlin looked at him. It was a strange choice of words. "Why odd?"

Graham shrugged as he finished his fries. "He's not mine."

He had lost her. Was Jake his wife's son, then? "I don't understand. I thought you said that Jake was your son."

"He is." Graham said it with such feeling, it made her wonder what was going on. "I adopted him. It was Celia's idea, really." And for that, he knew, he would always be grateful to her. It made for a very complicated situation.

"Celia's your wife?" Caitlin attempted to maintain a light, conversational tone. The word *wife* stuck to the roof of her mouth like wet bread.

He took a long pull from the bottle of soda. "Ex-wife."

Caitlin didn't attempt to put a name to the glimmer of buoyant emotion budding within her. "You're divorced?"

He nodded. "Two years."

There was no emotion in his voice. She couldn't tell if the collapse of his marriage had troubled him or not. Gray had become even more reticent since the days when they had been together.

But she hadn't really known him then, either, she reminded herself. If she had, what he had done wouldn't have shattered her the way it had. She would have anticipated it and been prepared instead of being so completely devastated.

"Nobody's fault," he added. "It was a mistake from the beginning." He glanced at Caitlin before taking another pull of his drink. "I'm good at making those kinds of mistakes."

She let his pregnant comment pass unquestioned, too tired to try to unravel the hidden implication of his words. "Why was your marriage a mistake?"

Graham was about to say that he had already said too much. He wasn't the type to bare his soul, and his friendships were few in number, though strong. But somehow, the words continued to come.

He shrugged philosophically, looking at the mouth of the bottle rather than at her.

"I married Celia because she said she was pregnant and the baby was mine." The faint outline of a self-deprecating smile curved his mouth. "I thought it was the right thing to do, give the baby a name."

That sounded like the Graham she'd once known. Had Celia taken advantage of him and lied? "And she wasn't pregnant?"

"No, she was. But she lost it."

He remembered how he had felt when the doctor had come out of the emergency room to tell him that Celia had miscarried. It was as if someone had physically punched him in the stomach. As if something special had been taken away from him before he had ever had the opportunity to hold it.

Graham set aside the empty bottle. "There were some complications." He distanced himself from the story. It did no good to feel guilty about it now. He wasn't responsible for what had happened to Celia. He had honestly tried to make things work between them. "The upshot of it was that she couldn't have any more children. And she was obsessed with having one. She begged me to go to a private adoption agency. I didn't want to, but…"

Graham shrugged, his voice trailing off. "I said yes. We adopted a half-Navajo boy."

Half Navajo. Like Gray, Caitlin thought. She wondered if he had seen himself in the boy and if that was part of the reason for his bond.

He dragged his hand through his hair. Celia had been like a completely different person back then, fussing over Jake. "For a while she was happy."

"For a while?"

Celia had had her reasons, he supposed. He could understand, up to a point. "Celia's childhood was pretty rocky. I suppose that's what drew us together in the first place." Celia was a full-blooded Navajo, abandoned by both parents and left to be raised by an aunt, who had beaten her. She'd been vulnerable and clingy, desperately looking for someone to love her. He had been nursing his hurt male pride and she had fed it. For a very small while, they had been good for each other. ''She didn't really know what she wanted.''

He wasn't sure what had come over him. He'd talked too much. Graham gave Caitlin a capsulated version of the rest of the story.

''Eventually, Celia decided that she wanted more out of life, that she didn't want to be married. Not to a cop, anyway. She wanted something better. So, she left.''

Caitlin couldn't picture walking out on Graham and a child. Commitments meant a great deal to her. ''Just like that?''

The indignation in her voice surprised him. ''No, there were some arguments first. But she left and I thought that was that.'' The divorce had been fast and uncontested. Celia had given up custody of Jake almost as if the boy had been hardly a footnote in her life. She had wanted her freedom that badly.

Caitlin recalled the conversation she'd overheard in her store. ''And now she's back?''

''Yeah.'' His tone was dismissive, abruptly cutting her off.

She wasn't going to let him do it this time. Determination etched the outline of her mouth. ''Don't tell me it's none of my business, Gray. You just saved my life.''

He looked at her, waiting to hear what that had to do with anything.

Caitlin waved her hands in frustration. ''Doesn't something in your heritage say we're bonded now?''

His expression was flat, unreadable. ''No.''

The man was infuriating. ''Well, pretend, then,'' she snapped. She blew out a breath and her voice softened. ''Tell me.''

He had no idea why he was sharing this with her, a woman who had walked out on him. Talking to Jeffers was one thing. Ben was his partner, his friend. They had been together for seven years and had shared a great deal in that time. Caitlin was someone he had thought he knew. And discovered he didn't.

He was here to guard her, nothing more.

Despite all logic, somehow the words seemed to continue

materializing on his tongue. "She's remarried, apparently very well, and she wants Jake." It sounded so simple and was so devastatingly complicated.

He rose, suddenly restless, and began to roam about the room. "Says she can give him a stable environment." Graham bit the words off. Celia's idea of stable translated into money. "She thinks she can buy her way back into Jake's affections, that money can negate everything she's done to him by leaving. But then, money was always important to her."

He didn't see the irony in it, did he? "Has a familiar ring to it," Caitlin murmured.

Graham stopped roaming aimlessly around and looked at her. "What?"

She hadn't meant to let that slip. He was hurting. The past was gone; there was no use in dredging it up. Caitlin shook her head, annoyed with herself. "Nothing. Go on."

He shrugged carelessly. "There's nothing to go on with. She wants to take me to court, sue for custody, if I don't agree to hand him over." The very words stuck in his throat.

Caitlin rose and crossed to him, drawn by the emotion he wasn't aware he was displaying. She laid her hand on his arm. "What do you plan to do?"

What every father would do. "Fight it." He saw sympathy in her eyes and instinctively withdrew. "I don't have much saved up to hire a lawyer, but there's got to be something I can do."

His words surprised her. "You don't have any money?" Her voice was incredulous. He wasn't frivolous. What had he spent it on?

That was what the argument had always been about. Money. "Honest cops usually don't, at least, not the kind that it would take for a prolonged court battle."

"The fifty thousand dollars is gone, then?"

Graham looked at her as if she had lost her mind. Maybe the stress of what had happened in the alley had got to her. "And what fifty thousand dollars would that be?"

The patronizing expression on his face annoyed her. She'd

been through too much today to keep a rein on her temper. "Don't play games with me, Gray. Don't you think I know?"

He kept his own temper on a choke hold, though it wasn't easy. She looked ready to do battle, and he hadn't the slightest idea about what. "Obviously, because you wouldn't have asked, but *I* don't know what you're talking about."

Caitlin threw up her hands, then crossed them before her chest. "All right, have it your way," she said evenly between her teeth. "The fifty thousand dollars that you asked for."

She still wasn't making any sense. Was this some sort of elaborate game Caitlin was playing? "And just who was I supposed to have asked for that kind of money?"

Caitlin glared at him. How far was he planning to take this innocent act? "My mother."

He was right. The attack in the alley had completely unhinged her. "I wouldn't ask your mother for the time of day, Caitlin."

Caitlin fisted her hands on her hips, her eyes on his. How could he stand there and deny it?

"You didn't come to her eleven years ago and say that if she wanted to be rid of you, she could, but that it would cost her?"

He stared at her as if she was reciting some sort of fantastic fairy tale. Her tone told him that she obviously believed what she was saying. Graham's eyes darkened. "What do you think?"

Face-to-face like this, she felt her conviction wavering. But he had left, damn him. Without her. What else was she to think?

"I didn't want to think that," she cried, frustration and long-pent-up hurt echoing in her voice. "But if you didn't ask her for the money, if she didn't buy you off, why weren't you there?" she demanded. Her eyes flashed as she came closer. "Why was I the only one left standing at the station after the last train for Las Vegas had left? You said you'd meet me there. I waited all night."

The details didn't make sense. "How could you have been standing at the station when you called my house and left a message with my uncle that you had changed your mind? That you were going away?''

Her eyes were wide, like huge turquoise flowers, as she listened to him. ''I never called. I never left any message.''

It was like trying to match two halves of a coin that refused to fit. ''I came looking for you, only to have your mother very smugly hand me a letter you had left behind.'' As he spoke, he relived it all—the humiliation, and worse than that, the pain. The gut-wrenching pain of losing her. ''The letter said you'd changed your mind.'' He took a breath, steeling himself. ''That you'd come to your senses and realized that this was wrong for both of us.''

He looked at her, challenging her to deny it. ''That you were leaving for Europe the next morning and I was to forget all about you. The way you were going to forget about me.''

Caitlin blanched. What was he talking about? She hadn't written any letter. She hadn't even told anyone about her plans. Least of all, her mother. ''And you believed that?''

He hadn't wanted to. He'd turned on his heel with Regina Cassidy's jeers ringing in his ears and stalked out. ''I did after I called the airport, pretending to be your father. I said I was looking for you, that you were a minor and you'd run away. They told me you were booked on a flight for Paris leaving at nine the next morning.''

Graham's eyes grew hard. ''Just like the letter said. So I figured the rest of the letter was true, too.''

She felt dazed. This had to be some sort of horrible nightmare. ''Yes, I was booked on a flight to Paris.'' She couldn't begin to fathom the expression on his face. It was dark and frightening and sad at the same time. A sob hitched in her throat. Oh, God, had it all been a misunderstanding, orchestrated by her mother? ''If you'd asked, you'd have found there were two seats in my name. That was my surprise for you. A honeymoon in Paris, right after the wedding.'' She closed her eyes to keep the tears back. Too many years had gone by to mourn now.

But she did. She mourned for everything that might have been and wasn't.

"I went alone after my mother told me that you'd asked for a check for fifty thousand to be out of my life." Why hadn't he come looking for her? Why? She had gone looking for him. "At first I refused to believe her. I drove all the way to your uncle's house, pounding on the door at six in the morning like some crazed loon, looking for you." She raised her head, trying to put it all behind her. "He told me you'd taken off." Her voice grew quiet to hide the hoarseness in it. "I figured it was with your newfound windfall."

How could she have thought that he would have sold what they'd had for money? He'd accepted what had happened because he thought it was better for her. It hadn't been for him. The first few months of life without her had been a living hell.

"I took off because I couldn't stand to be in the same city that you'd been in. There were just too many memories. I rode that motorcycle as far as I could, straight to California."

He shrugged. He'd been pretty crazed then, crazed with grief, with anger and alcohol. He didn't remember the trip at all. All he recalled was getting there, to the edge of a pier, and then suddenly stopping.

"Maybe I had some mixed-up idea of riding straight into the ocean with it, I don't know." He laughed shortly. "Somewhere along the line I decided that would make your mother too happy." He remembered looking down into the black waters, a moonless sky above him, and thinking that darkness had swallowed him up. It had taken a great deal to pull back. "So I didn't."

His tone changed as he gave her a clipped summary of the next nine years. "I came back, became a cop and met Celia. She was a friend of my cousin's. The rest I told you."

Caitlin felt as if the floor had dissolved beneath her feet. She was standing in midair, like some cartoon character, just waiting until she became conscious of the fact that there was nothing there before she began to fall. "Then you didn't leave me?"

What was the point of going over things? They couldn't pick up where they'd left off. He knew that. Too much time had passed. And the dreams had been cleared from his eyes. They didn't belong in each other's world. They never had.

"Not for the reasons you thought." He looked at her face and tried to remain unaffected. The young girl he had loved was still there. And because he'd loved her, he had to leave her alone. "But maybe your mother did us both a favor."

Right now she was contemplating justifiable homicide with her mother as the victim. How could he say that, after what she'd done to both of them?

"What?" she cried hoarsely.

Slowly he picked up the wrappers from the table and stuffed them into the bag, avoiding her eyes.

Coward's way, Redhawk, he upbraided himself.

"What you wrote—what your mother said you wrote— made sense after I calmed down and thought about it." He looked up at her. She was watching him quietly, working her lower lip. "You come from the right side of the tracks and I'm a half-breed. You have a place in this world and I don't, except for the one I make for myself." He shrugged. "That's why I like being a cop. I'm still on the outside, but I make a difference, anyway." Celia hadn't understood that. She had wanted him to be *someone.*

Caitlin stared at him for a long moment without being able to utter a sound. When she did, her voice was low, emotionless. She couldn't expect things to go back to the way they'd been just because things had been cleared up. A great deal of life had happened to both of them.

But his words still hurt. A small part of her would have wanted him to try to recapture what had been. When he had kissed her, she had almost been able to bridge the gap. Why hadn't he?

"You've gotten dumber since I knew you."

No, smarter. He shrugged carelessly, walking to the kitchen to throw away the bag. He was aware of her following. Graham looked around for the garbage and didn't see it. "Must be the blow to the head."

She took the sack from him. Opening the cabinet door beneath the sink, she tossed it into a tall receptacle. "What blow to the head?"

It ached a little now that he mentioned it. He'd thought he had jarred his teeth loose when he had hit the cement. "The one I got in the alley."

She raised her eyes, but she didn't see any telltale bumps or bruises forming. "You're hurt?"

"No." He was sorry he'd mentioned it. "Just a little shook up."

Like a terrier on the scent, Caitlin was circling him. On her toes, she reached up to the back of his head. She felt something sticky on her fingers. Looking at her hand, she saw a very thin trickle of blood.

She held up her hand for his benefit. "You're bleeding."

Graham pushed her hand away from his face. "Don't fuss, Caitlin. I don't like it."

"Tough. We're even. I don't like being strong-armed."

It was more than just concern. She had to busy herself somehow, occupy her mind until she could straighten things out in her own head. What he had just told her had turned her entire world upside down, banishing the careful balance of things she had arranged. Eleven years ago she had damned his soul for what had happened and her own for her stupidity in loving him. The rest of her life had been built on that foundation.

And now that she knew the truth, he was saying that it was for the best.

The hell it was.

Caitlin felt cheated. By her mother, by fate and by him.

Well, she couldn't do much about fate and she'd have to see about him, but her mother was another matter. She didn't know how yet, but her mother was going to pay for this, pay for ruining the happiness Caitlin knew in her heart was rightfully hers.

She wondered if it was legally possible for a daughter to publicly disown her mother. It had to be something public in order to affect the woman. Regina Cassidy could not care less how her daughter felt.

She took Graham's hand as if she were taking hold of a child and turned to lead him to the bathroom. But he wouldn't follow her. Caitlin looked at him impatiently. "You've got a cut on your head."

It wouldn't be the first time. Just a giant headache that would go away. He pulled his hand from hers. "It'll heal."

"Damn straight it will, but it might get infected." She took a far firmer grip on his hand, determined. "Come with me to the bathroom."

"You've gotten bossier." She'd been a girl when he had last seen her. A laughing-eyed girl who made him smile and feel good. She was a woman now. A woman who apparently knew her own mind. That didn't mean he had to agree with her.

"I've gotten my own self-image," she corrected him. Caitlin raised her chin. "No one walks on me anymore, Gray, or tells me what to do. Now, come on and let me take care of that."

Even his mother had never fussed over him. He wasn't accustomed to it and preferred to be left alone to deal with things on his own. "I said don't fuss."

Her eyes narrowed. She was through being tolerant. He'd gotten that cut saving her and she wasn't about to let it go.

"And I said come on." Her eyes challenged his, waiting. It was a small point, but it was a first step. She wasn't about to be ignored.

With a sigh Graham allowed himself be led off to the bathroom. "Don't see why this means so much to you."

"It makes me feel better, all right? Sit there." She indicated the rim of the bathtub.

"Definitely bossier," he murmured, but he sat.

"It would do you good to listen once in a while." She took out a tube of clear antiseptic from the medicine cabinet and carefully applied a tiny drop to his head along the cut.

Thank God it wasn't deeper, she thought. If it had been, he might have needed stitches. With a cotton swab she cleared the small area.

She knew it had to sting. Graham remained silent. She

winced for him. "Still stoic?" she asked as she recapped the tube.

He turned to look up at her. "Why, were you trying to hurt me?"

"No. I was just noting a fact." Caitlin replaced the anti-septic on the shelf. Her bravado wavered as she closed the door. Emotions spilled out, nearly drowning her.

When she turned around, he could see them all in her eyes. It was a struggle for him not to take her into his arms, to hold her. But it would only be starting something he hadn't the right to finish.

She cupped her palm along his cheek. "Oh, God, Gray, we wasted so much time."

Gently removing her hand, he shook his head. "No, your mother was right. Maybe for the only time in her life, but she was. It wouldn't have worked."

Caitlin felt as if she just couldn't get her footing this after-noon. She tried to understand what would make him say something like that. They had been so fiercely in love once. At least, she had.

"Why? Because your wife walked out on you?"

Maybe that was part of it. Maybe he just didn't believe in dreams. The only time he had was when he'd been with Cait-lin.

"My wife was a full-blooded Navajo. We had more in common than you and I do and it still didn't work out. I don't belong in either world, Caitlin, least of all yours."

Caitlin sighed. Gray was an idiot for thinking that way, but she had too much to assimilate right now to be able to argue with him and make sense.

"Come on, let me make you a better meal than what you just had. Something with substance in it. And then—" her voice lowered as if she was making a promise to herself "—I want to call my mother."

Summer storm clouds had looked less ominous than her expression did at this moment. "Why?"

He had to ask? Caitlin strode ahead of him out of the bathroom. "There are a few things that I need to get off my chest."

Her own woman or not, Caitlin looked too worn around the edges to get into a confrontation with her mother. The woman was a barracuda. Regina Cassidy would eat her alive. He didn't want to see that.

"Don't, Cait. She was only trying to do what was best for you."

Caitlin nearly laughed in his face. "That, astute detective, is where you're wrong. She was only trying to do what was best for *her*. That's a rule she's always lived by. Regina Cassidy first and everyone else a very distant second."

With that, Caitlin turned on her heel and led the way into the kitchen.

Chapter 8

Caitlin couldn't sleep.

She'd always been a good, sound sleeper, able to drop off as soon as her head hit the pillow. Tonight she lay awake for hours, watching shadows cast by the full moon flirting with the branches of the tree outside her window move back and forth along her ceiling.

She lay awake, tense, waiting, listening to every whisper of the wind, every creak of the house as it shrugged off the heat of the day. Every noise.

Scenes from this afternoon insisted on haunting her, playing themselves over and over again through her mind like an endless rerun.

Every time she closed her eyes she saw her attacker, a tall, handsome man, his ice blue eyes full of hate as he looked at her. She had managed to swing around in the alley, just before he'd pushed her into Gray, and had gotten a good look at him. Not his profile, like the first time, but his full face. Caitlin had needed to know what he looked like, needed to be able to scan a crowd and not be afraid that he was there somewhere, hidden in plain sight because she couldn't recognize who he was.

When Gray had shouted at the killer to stop, he had turned. For a brief second, when their eyes met, she'd seen the hate. He hated her and he didn't even know her.

Fear had passed down her spine like a cold, jagged icicle. In that instant she knew that her life meant nothing to the man. He would have snuffed it out as easily as he would have ground out a cigarette beneath the heel of his shoe. More easily.

She'd met her own mortality this afternoon and she was afraid.

Somewhere in the distance a dog suddenly howled. Caitlin bolted upright, ramrod straight, her heart thudding madly against her rib cage.

Her breath came in irregular snatches. Shaking, she tried to calm herself. It was just a dog, nothing more. She was trembling over a dog.

Caitlin scrubbed her face with her hands. It was no use. She wasn't going to get any sleep. She was too wound up. Tension shimmered through her, threatening to make her come unglued.

She hadn't even been able to vent any of it on her mother. She'd called Regina as soon as she'd finished cooking. Velma, one of the household staff members who remained on the premises while her mother traveled, had crisply informed her that Mrs. Cassidy had gone on a short cruise. Conveniently, Velma had no idea what ocean line her mother had booked passage on or how long she would be gone.

The hell she didn't, Caitlin thought angrily. Velma was following orders not to tell her. Her mother *always* left word where she could be reached in case someone of importance was looking to invite her to a high tea or a lavish party somewhere in the world.

But badgering Velma would have gotten Caitlin nowhere. Her mother selected her staff on their ability to keep their mouths closed. If they didn't, they were released. Instantly.

''Tell her her daughter wants to speak to her, Velma. That

I found out about the little charade she orchestrated eleven years ago and that we're going to have a long heart-to-heart about it when she returns. Tell her to borrow a heart so that she's armed.''

There had been silence on the other end and then the woman had nervously promised to relay the message ''if Mrs. Cassidy should call home.''

Angry tears of frustration had gathered in Caitlin's eyes. In her own way, despite everything, she loved her mother. And had Regina made any attempt to be one, even at this late date, Caitlin would have met her more than halfway.

But Caitlin's father had once told her that tigers couldn't change their stripes. And so it was with her mother. There would be no magical transformation into Donna Reed, accompanied by music by Rodgers and Hammerstein.

Caitlin was just going to have to accept that. She had hung up, far from satisfied. Nothing could have satisfied her, she supposed, but shouting would have helped a little.

There was no one to shout at now. And no way to rid herself of this horrid case of nerves that was threatening to overwhelm her. She could actually feel it swelling, growing as she sat in her bed, straining to make out the origin of different sounds.

She was going to drive herself crazy.

Annoyed with herself, Caitlin kicked aside the sheet covering her legs, bunching it up at the foot of the bed. She swung her legs over the side.

The air conditioner was set at seventy-eight. A nice, mild temperature, but she felt cold. Cold from the inside out. Caitlin ran her hands over her arms. She didn't think she was going to feel warm again until they finally caught this man. Until he was out of her life permanently.

If ever.

Restless, she got out of bed and walked out of the room to look in on Graham. If he was awake, maybe they could talk. Or play cards. Something. Anything to get her mind off the scenario that continued to thrust itself into her mind at every unguarded moment.

He heard her before she entered. Graham responded instantly to the sound of her bare feet treading lightly along the large, gray-blue tile. He was never completely asleep, even at home. Ever since he had been a child, there was something inside him that was always alert, always waiting to spring into action.

When he was five, there'd been a fire in the small house his father had rented. Graham had never forgotten the horror of waking up, surrounded by the all-consuming heat, by the flames that were taller than he was. He'd screamed, terrified, certain he was going to die. And then his mother had come running from the other room, running through the blaze to save him. She'd snatched him up and carried him off to safety, collapsing in the front yard.

Her left arm had gotten badly burned. The scars remained. His uncle had told him that they were her badge of courage.

His mother never talked about it and neither did he. But Graham was always aware of them beneath the long-sleeved blouses she wore. Aware, too, that she had given him life twice.

Hand on the gun that lay ready on the coffee table, Graham turned to see Caitlin standing in the doorway. Moonlight seeped into the hall from the kitchen, highlighting her body.

His breath stopped moving in his lungs.

She was wearing a nightgown that barely covered the tops of her thighs, the hem whispering along them the way his fingers itched to. He curled them into his palms. Graham felt something tightening within him and forced himself to relax.

Very carefully he lifted his hand from his gun.

"Can't sleep?"

She shook her head.

Standing there, she looked like every man's fantasy come to life. There was just so much restraint a man could be expected to have, and she was pushing his.

"Come here." He beckoned to her.

Caitlin approached almost shyly, wanting to be with him, wanting to be away.

The sofa was rumpled. She had made it up for him, placing

a blanket on top of the cushions and then covering it with a sheet. Blanket and sheet were now bunched together in a heap to the side, partially dripping down to the floor. Apparently he wasn't having any better luck sleeping than she was.

Caitlin pushed the tangled heap to the far end of the sofa. She felt guilty, making him sleep out here. By all rights he should be in his own bed, in his own home. "Not very comfortable, is it?"

He shrugged indifferently. "I've slept on a lot worse surfaces. This is fine." When pressed, he could catch a few winks anywhere, sleeping sitting up or lying down. It was all the same to him.

Caitlin sank down beside him and he tried not to notice how soft she felt. How good she smelled. The room was wide and airy, with vaulted, wooden beamed ceilings, yet all he was aware of was her.

He wasn't a boy anymore, he reminded himself. He was a detective with an assignment.

Caitlin shook her head, embarrassed over the way she was behaving. She was a full-grown woman acting like a frightened child. She flushed as she looked up at him.

"I know I'm being silly, but maybe it's the dark." Caitlin leaned against him, trying to keep her voice steady. "I'm scared, Gray."

It seemed natural, somehow, to place his arm around her shoulders. To hold her to him, as if the mere act could protect her from harm.

"No, you're not being silly. It's normal to be afraid. He almost killed you today." His error, Graham thought. He should never have let her out of his sight.

Caitlin turned to look at him, her long brown hair lightly brushing against his cheek, sending shock waves through him.

"Are you ever afraid?"

There was no honor in lying, no shame in the truth. "Yeah, sometimes."

She straightened, looking into his eyes. His answer surprised her. "Really?"

"Sure." He smiled at the wonder in her eyes. Did she think

he was so devoid of feelings after all? "I think of what might happen to me sometimes when I'm out there, working." But not often. If he did, he couldn't go out into the street, day after day. The thought would freeze him. "I'm careful, that's all. There's not just me to think about anymore. There's Jake. And my mother."

She liked that about him. Liked the way his eyes seemed to soften when he spoke of his son. Liked the fact that he had a sense of family. It made him wonderfully human for her.

Without thinking, he stroked his fingers along her arm as he held her to him and spoke. "I've got an insurance policy, but money isn't everything."

Having grown up without a father, he knew how empty that could be for a boy.

Caitlin smiled against him. God, but his warmth felt good to her. It seemed to envelop her. "Yes, I know."

Maybe she really did at that, he thought. She'd grown up with plenty of money, but with a viper for a mother. He had a feeling that Caitlin would have traded a great deal of it for a mother who lived up to the name.

"It's Jake I worry about mostly." And this haunted him, now more than ever, since Celia and her demands were breathing down his neck. "If I wasn't there for him, hell, Jake might turn out to be just like me."

She didn't like him running himself down. He'd always taken such a dark view of his life. She saw a far nobler man than he did.

Caitlin straightened again and looked up at him. "I would think that would be a plus."

He toyed with the end of a strand of her hair and laughed softly at her comment. "You didn't seem to think that yesterday."

Yesterday was a million years ago. "Yesterday I thought you sold me out for thirty pieces of silver. Or for fifty thousand pieces of paper."

No matter what she thought or didn't think, in reality nothing had changed. "I'm still the same man I was, Caitlin."

He was right. She had been too easily fooled by her mother.

She knew that now, but she had been so young and so very much in love. She had built her whole world around him and when she thought he'd left, it had all come crashing down.

Caitlin turned, tucking her legs beneath her and sitting on them. "I'm sorry. I should have realized that."

She was so close to him. So very close. His mouth felt as if he had been chewing on cotton. "Maybe you'd better go back to bed, Caitlin."

Was he angry at her after all? She'd just apologized. And he hadn't been the only one to be hurt. She had lost a large piece of her life, as well. "Why?"

His eyes swept over her slowly, unconsciously caressing her. He could feel his very skin tightening. "Because having you sit here dressed in light blue tissue paper is really testing me."

She felt the smile budding from her toes and rising to fill all of her, flowering in her eyes. "How are you scoring?"

He couldn't resist. He glided his knuckles along her arm. As she took a breath and held it, her breasts moved tantalizingly beneath the wafer-thin material, reminding him just how male he was. And how tempted.

"Close to zero, pretty soon."

If he thought he was frightening her away, he was wrong. Very, very wrong. Caitlin moved closer. "Funny, I would have said a hundred."

Caitlin leaned into him, her breasts just touching his arm, sending ripples of desire running through him like electricity jumping over wires. Very lightly she brushed her lips against his.

He gripped her shoulders, more to steady himself than to hold her back. His eyes warned her. "Cait, you're going to regret this."

She slowly moved her head from side to side, her eyes never leaving his. "Wrong. What I regret are all the years I've lost. All the years we've lost."

He had already told her that he thought it had worked out for the best. And he meant it. "You don't know what you're saying."

Her breath lingered on his mouth. "Then shut me up, Gray. You know how."

"Yeah, I know how." He continued to hold her at arm's length, fully aware that he was sinking quickly. "But that won't change anything."

This was wrong, wrong for her. Wrong for him to have a taste of what he couldn't ultimately have. The world hadn't changed any. He was still who he was.

She refused to have him talk her out of it. "Maybe for tonight, it will." She appealed to him. "I'm afraid, Gray. I need you to hold me."

It wasn't in him to refuse her. "You're making this so hard, Cait."

And then he couldn't reason with her, couldn't reason with himself. The ability had completely left him, washed away by the desire that he felt for her. The desire that had always remained within him, dormant, sleeping, but alive.

He slowly moved his hands underneath her nightgown, encircling her waist. Her skin was silky, smooth. Enticing.

Keeping a tight rein on the passions that flared in his blood, he brought her to him and sat her on his lap. For a moment he contented himself with just looking at her.

"You were the most beautiful thing I'd ever seen, from the moment I first laid eyes on you. More beautiful than a sunrise."

She remembered how he had wanted to share that sight with her. How wonderful he thought it was. Caitlin closed her eyes, overcome by the feelings pounding within her like waves on the beach at high tide.

She entwined her arms around his neck, bringing him closer. She caught her breath as she felt his thumbs tease the tips of her nipples. They hardened. Her head began to swim.

Yes, she thought. *Yes!*

This, this was all she had ever wanted. Gray holding her. Loving her. Only Gray. And it was finally going to happen.

His mouth covered hers, draining her, empowering her. Taking everything from her that she offered and returning it to her twofold. There were so many emotions churning within her, she lost count. Lost sight of everything but Gray.

Over and over again, like a starving man taking sustenance, his lips feasted on hers. He couldn't get enough of her, couldn't convince himself that this was real, that it was happening.

He'd never taken her before, only dreamed of it over and over again, even years after they had gone their separate ways. Sometimes at night she would creep into his dreams, soft and willing, and he would make love with her, only to wake up beside Celia, filled with regret.

And guilt.

And now Caitlin was here, real, flowing like hot, molten lava through his hands. He couldn't touch her enough, couldn't hold her enough. He wanted to steep himself in her.

If, by some horrid twist of fate, it was another dream, then he prayed that he'd never wake up.

He couldn't get enough of her. His hands touched, possessed, molded, worshiped, forging a path for his mouth to follow. He kissed, suckled, teased. She tasted of all things wondrous and willing.

Sweet, dark, tempting.

His.

Caitlin groaned as he gently pushed her down on the sofa. He pressed a kiss against her throat and she felt her pulses throb all along her body, wanting him. Demanding him. She was ripe for him, waiting all these long, barren years for this. For him.

Impatient, her mouth still sealed to his, Caitlin tugged at his shirt, pulling it free of his waistband. Her hands splayed along his skin. Smooth, heaving, it felt hot to the touch, burning her fingers.

Burning her soul.

How she wanted him!

He raised himself on his elbow, hovering over her, defining the perimeters of her world. He looked down into her face. Her eyes were huge, dazed, her mouth mussed from the imprint of his. He'd never wanted anyone so much in his life.

"Would you be more comfortable in your bed?"

Her arms remained around his neck, afraid that if she released them, he'd vanish, like some elusive, magic butterfly. "Not alone."

"I wasn't thinking of leaving you alone." He couldn't if he tried. Not now, when she had raised the fires of his soul so high.

He lifted her into his arms and carried her to her bedroom.

Vainly trying to hold back tears of joy, Caitlin wrapped her arms around his neck and pressed her face against his shoulder.

He felt the dampness through the material as he brought her to her bed. She'd changed her mind, he thought. "Caitlin?"

"Shh." Her breath wafted along his arm. "If you ask me one more time if I'm sure, I won't be responsible for my actions."

He set her down gently. "I don't think either one of us is responsible right now." He knew if he was thinking clearly, rationally, he wouldn't have allowed things to go this far.

But he wasn't thinking clearly. He wasn't really thinking at all.

Caitlin knelt on her bed, her arms still around his neck, her body eager, primed, calling to his. And her eyes said things to him that her mouth couldn't.

"Think again." Her lips whispered along his, teasing, tantalizing, breaking his stamina. "Make love with me, Gray," she urged softly, like sin floating along his flesh. She drew her arms away, giving him his freedom. Holding him captive with her eyes. "Make love with me the way you should have years ago. Love me, Gray."

He knew if he did, if he truly let himself love her again, it would be his downfall. And, very possibly, hers.

His eyes still on hers, Graham pulled the shirt off his body, tossing it aside, then unbuckled his belt. He moved as if he were in a dream.

Laying her hands over his, she stopped him before he could continue. Her eyes remained on his. Caitlin coaxed the hook free at the top of his gray trousers, then slowly slid the zipper down with the tip of her forefinger. Down the length of him. She felt him shudder slightly beneath her hand and her smile ripened.

"Where did you learn to do that?" he asked hoarsely.

"Nowhere." Her answer was honest. "I'm self-taught. As of this moment."

Her words hardly registered in the haze of desire surrounding him. Graham wanted to make love with her the way she deserved. Gently, reverently, slowly.

But demands were slamming through him like the bubbles in a shaken champagne bottle, begging for release. Begging him to take her quickly before his body incinerated.

He'd never been ruled by passions before. He'd always been clearheaded. Yet passion held him prisoner now. He felt weak as a baby, strong as the legendary gods of his mother's religion. He was everything.

Because he was with Caitlin.

Caitlin's hands were hot, fevered, as they touched him, coaxing the rest of the material from him until trousers and underwear slid the rest of the way down along his muscular legs.

And were discarded.

Graham stood before her, naked as the day he'd been born. His body looked as if it had been carved out of stone, fashioned by a benevolent god.

Just for her.

He was magnificent. And just for now, she thought, he was hers.

Her breath catching again, she slid her hands slowly along the outline of his body as if she were molding him to an image in her mind.

Graham caught her hands, afraid that if Caitlin continued to glide her fingers along him that way, he'd lose what little reason, what little restraint he still had left.

"Not too fast, Cait," he cautioned when she looked at him in surprise.

She wanted to smile, but couldn't. "After eleven years, this isn't fast," she whispered. But she let him still her hands.

Very carefully Graham began to raise the hem of her nightgown. He teased it up along her body inch by fraction of an inch, as if this were some endurance test he'd set for himself, a test he had to pass in order to be at peace with himself.

He saw the desire flare in her eyes and knew it was mirrored within his soul.

Soon, Cait, soon.

His breath grew short, ragged, as he continued to raise her nightgown along her silken skin.

The throbbing, the wanting, increased. Caitlin thought she would melt into a puddle, a hot, yearning puddle at his feet before he was finished. Finally he raised the nightgown up and over her head and threw it aside.

Caitlin cleaved her body to his and then all restraint was gone.

Mouths sealed to one another, they fell back on her bed, a tangle of limbs. A tangle of emotions and needs.

Graham kissed her over and over again, as his blood rushed in his ears and his breath grew shorter and shorter. Grasping her hands in one of his, he held them over her head as he moved over her.

His eyes were on hers. Hers were wide, absorbing him. Looking at him.

As if she knew he needed that. Needed to have her look at him while they made love.

Her breasts rubbed urgently against his skin, cream against bronze. He moved his head down and suckled, teasing the tip of one with his tongue, then the other. He felt her squirm beneath him, hardening him until his desire was so strong it threatened to break free at any moment.

Caitlin arched against him and then there was no turning back. He knew he couldn't have even if he'd wanted to. And he didn't want to. The need was too strong, beyond all reason.

As he began to enter her, a small whimper broke free from her lips and his eyes widened. He stopped.

"You're—"

Oh, no, they'd come too far for him to stop now. She wouldn't let him stop now.

"Yours, Gray. I've always been yours." Her arms tightened against him and she arched her hips up even farther.

He entered, unable to hold back. Sheathed in her, he felt as if he'd finally come home.

The next moment passions drummed through him and he began to move, afraid of hurting her no matter what he did.

The pain melted away in the heat until it was gone as if it had never existed. She responded, her body urgent beneath his.

The decisions were all taken from him as they took the journey together, scaling the highest peak two lovers could.

Chapter 9

The journey they took together was wild and wondrous, and over all too soon. Graham could feel Caitlin's heart hammering beneath his, as if it were really one heart cleaved in two.

But it wasn't, and he knew it. To believe anything else would be to play the fool. They were far too different to make it work for long.

Slowly his breathing evened. Very carefully Graham rolled off and settled in beside her. Euphoria retreated and disappeared.

Reality returned with a one-two punch.

Damn, what had he been thinking of? Where was his self-control? He shouldn't have let this happen. No matter how much he had wanted her, how much he ached, he shouldn't have let things go this far. He was supposed to be guarding her, for pity's sake.

When he had taken off for California, he had tottered on the edge without any thought to ever waking up tomorrow. The bottle had called to him, offering solace. The temptation of drowning himself in its amber liquid and forgetting all about Caitlin had been so strong it had all but rattled his teeth. It had almost sucked him in.

But somehow he had found the ability to resist, to hold fast against the overwhelming urges. Why couldn't he have done the same with her?

The sound of their breathing drifting through the air was all that she heard. But Caitlin sensed something ominous; she could feel the silence creeping along her skin like a long-legged spider.

When she turned her head toward him, Graham was looking at her. His eyes were fathomless again.

Why can't I ever know what you're thinking, Gray? Even now?

But things had never been easy with Gray. There was no way to find out what was on his mind except to ask. "What?" she prompted.

With every passing second the silence was eating away at her, making small holes in her confidence that were growing into large ones.

Beyond the annoyance at his own lack of control was a core of guilt. He hadn't known, wouldn't have guessed that that was her first time.

"Why didn't you tell me?" Had he known, he would have found the strength to back away.

Caitlin stiffened. Suddenly she didn't feel nude, she felt naked. And there was a world of difference between the two.

"Tell you what?" There was an edge in her voice.

He fairly growled out the words. "That you were a virgin."

Another mistake that was his fault. Once he had wanted to be her first lover. Her only lover. Now he knew it wasn't right. There couldn't be any special place in her life for him. It wouldn't be fair to her.

Caitlin stared at him, hardly breathing. She couldn't put a name to what she was feeling at the moment. But the euphoria was a long distance away.

Had he been disappointed because she was inexperienced?

The thought tasted bitter on her tongue. "What part of the conversation would it have fit into? 'Hello, Gray, how are

you? By the way, I'm still a virgin.'" Her eyes darkened.
"Or maybe, 'Gee, Gray, did you know that I never—'"

He cut her off with a single word, framed in amazement.
"How?"

Indignant, confused, she rose up on one elbow and looked
at him. What was he asking her? "How am I still a virgin?"

"Yes."

Tugging, she pulled the sheet up from the foot of the bed
and covered herself. "The usual way, Gray." Embarrassment
urged her not to look at him. Hurt pride demanded that she
did. "I don't see how that's such a mystery to you."

But it was. A total mystery. Unable to help himself, he
touched her hair, his fingers lightly skimming the length of it
as it spilled over her shoulder. Like dark, rich honey.

Graham felt control slipping away again. "You're a beautiful woman, Caitlin. You should have…" His voice trailed
off.

She raised her eyes to his, beginning to understand. "Made
love with someone else by now?"

He realized that what he was feeling was jealousy. He hated
the thought of someone else's hands on her. But it would have
been only natural.

"Yes."

*Would you have cared if someone else had, Gray? Would
you?* She wanted him to care, the way she cared that he had
married someone else.

She blew out a breath and shrugged, looking away.
"Maybe I didn't care enough about anyone to make love with
them. Maybe," she said slowly, "after you walked out of my
life, that didn't seem very important anymore."

Caitlin turned her head and looked at him. "Or maybe I
just couldn't share myself." She swallowed, knowing, as always, that she had revealed too much and he nothing at all.
She forced her voice to sound casual. "Take any of the
above."

He'd hurt her by asking. It was there in her eyes, even
though her mouth was hard. He hadn't meant to. Hurting her
seemed to be second nature to him.

"I'd rather take you." Slowly he skimmed his hand along her shoulder. His fingers urged away the sheet she held against her.

His gaze warmed her. Caitlin's somber expression dissolved into a smile. She didn't understand him, but she did understand herself. She knew exactly what she was feeling for him.

Caitlin turned her body toward him. "No problem there."

"Oh, there are problems, Cait," he assured her solemnly. "Plenty of problems." He combed his hand through her hair, his eyes already making love to her again. "But I don't want to think of them now."

"That makes two of us." Shifting, Caitlin opened her arms to him. Inviting him. Enticing him. "Hold me, Gray, hold me and pretend everything is going to be just fine." The thought whispered seductively along his temples. "And then maybe it will be."

She'd always had this optimism about her. It was what had drawn him to her to begin with. She was like this pure, white light, shining on him, chasing away the darkness of his soul. For a while he had allowed himself to believe the way she did.

But he knew better now. The world wasn't a kind, forgiving place for outcasts. What kind of a life could he offer her?

Still, for the time being, as the world slept and the darkness was kept outside the magic circle she had drawn around them, he could indulge her, and himself. He could pretend the way she wanted him to.

He gathered her to him, heat seeking heat. Heat fueling heat.

As he kissed her, Graham felt her mouth curving into a smile beneath his lips.

Raising his head, he framed her face with his hands. He was right, she was the most exquisite thing he had ever beheld. "What are you grinning about?"

Her smile was wide, guileless, like a child discovering a candy store. "I like it."

Her smile coaxed one from him without his even being conscious of it. "What?"

"Making love. I like making love." Her eyes softened as the love she felt for him entered into them. She touched his face lightly with her fingertips. "It was well worth waiting for."

He didn't answer.

Caitlin hesitated. Maybe she *had* disappointed him. "Was I all right? I mean—"

He laid his finger over her lips. "You were wonderful," he assured her. Before she could ask another question, he pressed a kiss to her shoulder, then moved slowly to her throat.

She felt herself slipping away again. The world was being reduced to a small opening the size of the head of a pin.

"The same goes for you," she whispered, her arms tightening around his neck.

Waves of ecstasy were beginning to flow through her again.

"How would you know?" He laughed and she felt the vibrations along her breast. His tongue branded her, skimming, teasing. Caitlin's skin tingled. "You have nothing to compare it to."

"Some things," she told Graham as she arched into him, into his kiss, "you just know. They're an absolute."

She was absolutely precious.

Maybe he could make tonight last, he thought, holding her to him. Maybe somehow, he could outrun the dawn.

At the very least, he could try.

Sleep left Caitlin slowly, like shadows being replaced by sunshine. She felt like a contented, well-fed cat, curled before a warm fireplace.

Smiling to herself, she turned into Graham. The space beside her was empty. Startled, Caitlin sat up, instantly awake. He wasn't there.

"Gray?"

There was no answer. Nervous, she rose quickly. The tangled sheet was on the bare, hardwood floor. She nearly tripped on it as she reached for her nightgown. Throwing it on, she hurried from the room.

"Gray?"

One moment the small hallway was empty, the next, Graham was in it, his gun drawn in response to the urgency in her voice. Caitlin gasped, flattening herself against the wall, her heart fluttering like the wings of a hovering hummingbird.

Swallowing a curse, he holstered his gun. For a second he had thought that the killer had got in somehow.

It took her a minute before her knees solidified again. Caitlin left the shelter of the wall. "Is every morning like this with you?"

He shrugged, trying to ignore the fear that had seized him when he heard her cry out his name. "You sounded frightened."

"I was." She relaxed a little. It was all right. He was here with her. "I thought you were gone."

"I got up an hour ago." He wished that she had put on something else, or at least pulled a robe over it. Her nightgown left nothing to the imagination. And everything. Echoes of last night padded through his mind on soft paws.

He nodded toward the kitchen behind him. "I was just going to call you. Breakfast is ready. It's not much, but it's hot."

Graham abruptly turned and walked back into the kitchen. If he stood beside her for another moment, he knew he was going to kiss her again. And that would be another mistake.

She smiled as she followed him into the kitchen. "Talk about service."

He glanced over his shoulder, placing the width of the gray-tiled counter between them. "It's not the kind you're used to."

She wished that this fictitious image of a princess wasn't shimmering between them. "It's the kind I like. Besides, for the last eleven years, I've basically been on my own."

He picked the skillet up from the burner and emptied the remaining contents onto a plate. He'd eaten his breakfast earlier. "That long?" The toast had just popped. He swiped a knife with butter on it over the two pieces, making marginal contact. Done.

She nodded in answer to his question. Did he have any idea how endearing he looked, attempting to be domestic?

"College, and then my own business. I couldn't stay at the house after I returned from Paris."

Not with her mother living there. Regina had wanted to take control of her life again and Caitlin had absolutely refused to allow it. Regina had assumed it was a passing phase. She was greatly put out to learn that it wasn't.

"Especially not after Daddy died." He'd been her only ally. "Home wasn't home to me anymore. I had to find my own niche."

Like him, Graham thought. Except that Caitlin wasn't like him. She was as far from him as the stars were from the earth.

Caitlin dragged her hand through her hair, blinking the last remnants of sleep from her eyes. With a contented sigh she sat at the counter and looked at the plate he set before her. Toast and eggs. Both were slightly burned around the edges.

Like him, she mused.

She curled her hands around the steaming cup of coffee he'd poured for her. "So, what's on the agenda? Am I allowed to go to work?"

He would rather she stayed at home, in protective custody, but he knew she'd go stir-crazy if he attempted that. It was something he could relate to. He knew what it felt like to be caged. The only difference was that his cage was invisible; it was his soul that was locked up. Still, the bars were real, and just as confining. Maybe more so.

Coffee cup in hand, Graham slid onto the stool next to hers, carefully keeping his eyes on her face. "I'll take you to work as soon as you're ready, then my partner will take over."

Caitlin wondered if she actually stiffened or if it only felt as if she had. She didn't like what she heard in his voice. "But I'll see you again?"

He contemplated the inside of his cup. Black liquid shimmered up at him. Black, like the future he could offer her.

Maybe he could talk to the captain. "Caitlin, that might not be—"

God, but he was dense. "You say 'wise' and you're going to be one sorry police detective when I get through with you."

He laughed. The image of Caitlin pounding her fists on him tickled him. "Quite the little wildcat, aren't you?"

She raised her chin pugnaciously, but her eyes shone. "When I have to be." The light abated slightly. "I wouldn't have been able to survive with Mother if I hadn't turned into something other than the scatter rug she was grooming me to be."

Absently, she took a sip of the coffee. It was strong. A great deal stronger than anything she would have brewed, but it helped brace her.

"What about you? Are you going home to see Jake after you drop me off?" She tried to make her question sound conversational, but after all this time she was hungry for every single scrap of his life. She wanted to be a part of it. Permanently. Not just because she was an assignment.

He nodded, then drained his own cup. He set it down on the counter. "Stopping there for a minute." They were back on professional footing. He could handle that. Graham turned on the stool, facing her, his hands laced before him. "I'm going to the precinct to see if they've gotten any information on the license plate I called in. Maybe we've made some headway finding that scum." There wasn't a hint of a smile on his face, in his voice. "I want this to be over for you."

He said it as if he meant that to include everything. A chill of a different nature passed over her. He regretted last night. She could tell.

Caitlin searched for something else to talk about. Everything that had happened between them was too new, too shaky, like a freshly painted wall whose color had yet to set.

She thought of Jake. "What about Celia?"

He raised a brow. Where had that come from? "What about Celia?" he asked cautiously.

Why was he taking that tone with her? As if he didn't trust her. As if they were strangers and she had stumbled onto hallowed ground. "What are you going to do about the custody issue?"

He wished she wouldn't concern herself with that. He'd been an idiot to mention it to her. "I already told you…"

Impatience drummed through Caitlin with long, bony fingers. What he had told her was that he didn't have the money to take care of the matter properly. That wasn't a plan, that was a problem.

A problem she wanted to help with.

"I could call my lawyer." Sensing his displeasure, Caitlin picked up speed. "He's very good and he might—"

Graham shook his head. This had to be done his way. "Caitlin, I don't want your lawyer." When she opened her mouth to protest, he cut her off. "And I don't want your money," he told her sharply, "if that's what you were going to offer next."

He was trying to push her away. Why? What was wrong with him?

"How about a course in humility?" Graham merely looked at her, waiting for an explanation. "Down-scaling your pride." Caitlin looked at him pointedly. "If you're not careful, it'll make you lose Jake."

"Let me worry about Jake."

Caitlin sighed. There was no reasoning with him right now. He probably felt uncertain about what had happened between them and that was coloring everything. Gray had always had a tendency to study something from every angle, looking for the flaw.

"All right, but I'm here if you need me." She glanced at her watch and stifled a yelp. She hadn't realized it was this late. "But not for long." Quickly she slid off the stool. The nightgown fluttered down around her. "I've got to get ready."

He looked at the plate she'd left almost untouched. "What about breakfast?"

She forced a broad smile to her lips as she ducked out. "It was delicious."

Yeah, right. Graham rose, her plate in his hand. "Cait," he called after her.

Her hand on the jamb, she looked in. "Yes?"

"That nightgown you're wearing. Is it one of yours?" He felt as if he was tripping over his own tongue. He shouldn't have said anything. "I mean, from the store."

This time her broad smile was genuine. "Yes."

Graham nodded, turning his back to her as he cleared off her plate. What was left of her breakfast slid into the garbage.

"You must get a lot of repeat business," he muttered, barely audible.

Caitlin bit back a laugh. Maybe things were brighter than they seemed. "Yes, I do. I'll be back in a minute," she promised.

The sound of her laughter, light, airy, wafted back to him from the hall.

He was in over his head, he thought grimly, and he was going to have to swim for shore.

Fast.

Thirty minutes later, when they drove up the block where the shop was located, Caitlin suddenly leaned forward, squinting at the building. The lights were on.

Had Kerry forgotten to turn them off last night? Or was someone inside the shop? The thought pushed its way forward, unsettling the happy feeling she'd been nursing.

She turned toward Graham. "It's early."

He parked the car. Graham understood what she was saying. "Why don't you wait in the car?" he suggested, getting out.

"Alone?" He had to be kidding. Caitlin was out of the car half a beat after he was, joining him on the sidewalk. "I don't think so."

He walked in first, mentally cursing the bell that went off announcing his entrance.

At the sound, Kerry popped up from behind the counter like bread ejecting out of a toaster. Her arms were loaded down with merchandise. The surprised look on her face melted when she saw them.

"Oh, hi, you startled me." Dramatically letting out a breath, she deposited the gay profusion of bras on the counter.

Graham looked away. There weren't many places in this store a man could look without feeling awkward.

Caitlin pushed past him, setting her purse down behind the counter. "We could say the same thing to you." It was too early for her to be in the shop. Kerry liked to sleep in. There were times in college when Kerry had seemed hermetically sealed to her pillow. "What are you doing here?"

Kerry shrugged. "Well, I didn't think you were coming in today, so I thought I'd get a jump start on opening up the shop. You know what a slug Eva can be at times."

Caitlin looked at Kerry gratefully, politely ignoring the comment about Eva. "Thanks for coming in so early, but I'm here and I intend to stay."

Amusement lifted the corners of her mouth as Kerry looked at Graham. "Couldn't keep her home, huh? Ever think of tying her up?"

A touch of humor entered his eyes as he glanced at Caitlin. "The thought crossed my mind." Graham looked at his watch. It was almost eight. "I'm going to make a call."

He was already heading to the back room. Caitlin followed. "Jake?"

That was one of the calls he was going to make. He didn't feel like elaborating. "Yeah."

Caitlin stood in the doorway, watching as he tapped out the numbers on the keypad. "Who stays with him when you're out like this?"

"My mother." He hit the last two numbers. "She lives with us now."

When she had first met Graham, his mother lived on the reservation near the Utah border. He had come to Phoenix to live with an uncle while he attended high school, trying to find his place in a predominant white man's world. "Has she been living with you for a long time?"

The telephone was still ringing. He wondered where his mother was. She was an incredibly early riser. "Since Celia left.'' He turned his back to her as he heard the receiver being picked up on the other end. "Hello? Jake? Hi, it's Dad.''

Feeling as if she was suddenly intruding, Caitlin withdrew. She released the curtains. They sashayed across the jamb and sill, settling into place.

When she turned around, her eyes met Kerry's. Kerry looked as if she was about to burst as she approached her. "Anything happen last night?''

Caitlin shook her head. "The killer didn't show up again.''

"I'm relieved, but I wasn't talking about the killer.'' Kerry looked over her shoulder to the back room. The low murmur of Graham's voice was barely audible in the background. They could talk for a few minutes without being overheard. "Did anything happen with him?''

Caitlin bit her lower lip, but didn't answer. She didn't have to.

Kerry's grin was wide, taking over her entire face. "It did, didn't it?'' she asked in a hushed whisper. Clapping her hands together, she almost laughed out loud, very pleased with herself. "I knew it. I just knew it. I knew it would.''

Caitlin refused to confirm Kerry's assumption. "I didn't say anything.''

"You don't have to.'' Kerry stood back and studied her best friend's face. "For a woman who was almost killed yesterday, you're positively glowing.'' Kerry seemed beside herself with glee.

You would have thought that Kerry had slept with Gray instead of her, Caitlin mused.

Kerry gripped Caitlin's arm as she lowered her voice. "How was he?''

Caitlin pointed to the lingerie still scattered on the counter. "Kerry, the bras need rearranging.''

Kerry ignored the colorful heap. "Cait, I always tell you.'' She pouted. "And it's all been one-sided until now.''

Refusing to indulge her fantasies, Caitlin remained silent on the subject.

Undaunted, Kerry laughed. "Have it your way. I'll get you

to talk yet." She squeezed Caitlin's hand affectionately. "I am so happy for you."

Caitlin looked toward the back room. Graham was still in there. She thought of the way he'd looked this morning. He was trying to distance himself from her.

"I'd tone it down a notch or two if I were you. I have no idea how he feels about this."

Kerry smiled smugly as she began neatly folding the bras. "I do."

That made Kerry one up on her, Caitlin thought. "Oh, really?"

"Sure." She gestured toward the back with her free hand. "Just look at the way he looks at you. There's a lot going on behind those dark eyes of his."

"There always was," Caitlin said quietly. The trouble was, she didn't know what. Only that it had a habit of getting in the way. His view of life was far too dark.

Rousing herself, Caitlin got down to business. There was a lot to do before they opened. But as she worked, she kept one eye on the back room.

When he finally walked out again, Graham's expression was grimmer than it had been.

Abandoning the display, Caitlin hurried toward him. "What's wrong?"

He'd spoken to his mother after he had talked to Jake. And then telephoned the lawyer the department had put him in contact with. Neither conversation had been heartening.

But it was his problem to work out, not hers. She had enough to handle. "Nothing that concerns you."

Her eyes narrowed even as she lowered her voice to keep her words from carrying to Kerry. "Don't start again. Just tell me."

He supposed she'd carry on until he did. "Somehow, Celia's lawyer managed to get an early court date. There's a preliminary hearing in the judge's chambers set for next week."

The department's legal-aid lawyer had told him something that the man thought might help the situation, but it wasn't anything Graham wanted to share with her. Besides, it wasn't really possible. There just wasn't enough time.

Caitlin grew concerned. If Celia's new husband was well-off, he could afford to hire a good lawyer, one who would know how to sway the decision in her favor. Sympathy always tended to be on the mother's side.

"Gray…"

He didn't want her sympathy. Or her pity. Graham deliberately looked past her head. A beige car was parking behind his sedan. Talk about the cavalry riding to the rescue.

"Ben's here." Graham hardly looked at her as he headed for the door. "I'll be back later."

Caitlin stood watching him as he walked out of the store. She felt so frustrated she could scream. The big dumb jerk just had too much pride, she thought.

Chapter 10

Midmorning traffic moved through the downtown area like heavy syrup. Impatience hummed through Graham. He jockeyed for position, maneuvering the sedan into any decent opening that presented itself. For once he was grateful he wasn't driving his Caddie.

There was too much to do today to relax.

He'd spent exactly fifteen minutes with his son before he had to be on his way again. It was all the time that he had to spare.

Usually the heat didn't bother him. Today it did, annoying him as it wafted under his skin. Surrendering, he turned on the air-conditioning and tried to loosen up. He succeeded marginally.

In the past couple of days it had felt as if he had one foot in the stirrup, trying to mount a horse that was running down the path at a full gallop. Everywhere he turned there was something urgently calling for his attention, demanding to be placed first.

He had to be in criminal court at ten to testify on an arrest he'd made two months ago. There was a meeting scheduled with his lawyer about Jake at one o'clock. Jeffers had told him just before he left Caitlin's shop that the DMV had come up with a name on the license plate he'd called in yesterday.

And Caitlin was playing along the planes of his mind like a wind song across the desert.

The car in front of his pulled up short and Graham jammed on his brakes, narrowly avoiding locking bumpers. He let out a shaky breath, combing his hand through his dark hair. He had to stop letting his thoughts distract him like this.

Graham sighed as he pulled into the police department's parking lot, leaving the sedan parked beside his own pink Cadillac. In all the excitement, he hadn't had time to bring it home.

Maybe tomorrow. He had his priorities, but there just didn't seem to be enough of him to go around.

One thing at a time, Redhawk, one thing at a time. Yes, but which one thing?

The minutes seemed to be trickling by as he hurried up the steps to the squad room on the second floor. Graham glanced at his watch. Eight-fifty. He had less than an hour to see if anyone had come up with any information on Caitlin's would-be kidnapper.

He pushed open the door to the squad room. It was already teeming with activity. Detectives were taking statements from suspects, from victims, pushing papers around. Patrolmen mingled with plainclothesmen. He wondered if crime ever took a holiday.

There was nothing filled in after Chambers's name on the sign-out board. That meant he was in. Graham scanned the room, looking for the older detective. Jeffers had said the captain had assigned Chambers to track down the license plate number and see where the trail led.

Chambers wasn't hard to spot, even in this milling crowd. He was at his desk on the far side of the room. Graham cut through the press of passing bodies and crossed to him.

A greasy white-and-red wrapper was spread open on one corner of Chambers's desk, sharing space with three opened files, a magazine on recreational vehicles and a map of New

Mexico that from the creases on it had eternally eluded proper refolding. The breakfast burrito that had come in the wrapper was on its way to being history.

Andy Chambers had blond hair the color of bleached wheat left out in the sun. It served to make his red face look all the more flushed. His blood pressure had made the betting pool. There was nothing Chambers liked better than eating, unless it was solving a case. He was embroiled in both at the moment.

He looked up when Graham sat next to his desk. "What's up?" The question was muffled as he swallowed the last of the burrito.

Graham pushed toward Chambers the paper napkin that was peering out from beneath the wrapper. The man absently wiped his mouth, already thinking about his next meal.

"Jeffers said you might have something for me."

Chambers threw the napkin into his overflowing wastepaper basket and sent the wrapper in after it. The grin on his face was broad and genuine as he looked at Graham. Andy Chambers loved his work and it showed.

He nodded. "Christmas comes early in the desert."

Chambers liked to talk and draw things out. Graham didn't. "Translation?"

Chambers enjoyed unveiling clues with a flourish. This morning he obviously had no takers. "You know, Redhawk, you can be a real downer sometimes." He began reshuffling his files.

"I'll work on my social skills." Somewhere in the distance a door slammed. He wondered if the captain was having a hard day. Martinez didn't believe in keeping things in and letting them eat away at the lining of his stomach. Maybe he should give it a try. Graham fixed Chambers with a demanding look. "What do you have?"

Chambers riffled through the folders on his desk, the object of his search apparently eluding him. "That car that almost ran you down? It belongs to a big-time operator in California." He slanted a look at Graham to see how he took the news.

They were finally getting somewhere. Graham sat up, alert. "Name?"

"Garreo. Thomas."

It was a name Graham was vaguely familiar with. Black-market babies, drugs. Major slime. "Got a location on him?"

"Yeah."

There was a catch. He could hear it coming. "Can we pick him up?"

A touch of black humor curved Chambers's wide mouth. "Sure. In a pine box. He's dead."

Damn. Graham sighed loudly, passing a hand over his face. So who had been driving the car? And where did that leave them? Square one?

Momentarily abandoning his search, Chambers seized his opportunity. He raised his forefinger dramatically. "But—the number-one man in his organization, Horace Taylor, fits the description you and the lady whose lovely body—" his eyes sparkled "—you're guarding gave us. Horace obviously took possession of his boss's car after he was iced."

"Horace?" Graham repeated. "Nobody's named Horace anymore."

Chambers nodded, resuming his search for the file. "Could account for his lousy disposition." He sighed.

What the hell was Chambers looking for? "So where is he?" Graham asked impatiently.

Redhawk would live a lot longer if he learned to take things easy. "Whereabouts are being checked out now, even as we speak," Chambers drawled. He leaned forward, grinning, clearly enjoying center stage. Tiny dimples appeared at each corner of his mouth. "He has a little thing going on the side with this exotic dancer at The Feel Good Inn. Captain hopes she might lead us to him. There's a tail on her now." Chambers laughed under his breath as he opened a drawer and took out a candy bar. "Juarez thinks he's falling in love."

Detective Juarez and his overactive libido were a matter of record. They weren't his concern. Caitlin was. "We have a picture of this guy?"

"Yeah, somewhere." Chambers shifted over a stack that looked to be collecting dust.

Graham shook his head. He was far from neat, but clutter like that got in his way. How could Chambers work like this? "Don't you ever clean this mess up?"

Chambers took no offense. He paused to peel back the wrapper on his candy bar and took a healthy piece. "Yeah. Sometimes. Christmas. Easter."

Triumph telegraphed through him as he found what he was looking for under the recreational vehicle magazine.

Grinning, he took out the black-and-white photograph from the folder and held it up to Graham. "Leap year," he added.

That Graham could readily believe. In the past seven years he recalled seeing Chambers's desk cleared only twice. And one of those times had been when Chambers was out on disability for a gall bladder operation. Everyone else had taken over his cases.

"That sounds about right." Holding the photograph in his hand, Graham looked down at the face depicted there. Bull's-eye. It was their man. He rose, pocketing the photograph in his jacket. "I'm going to take this back to show Caitlin."

Chambers grinned so hard his eyes seemed to melt into his round face, leaving behind only tiny slits. "That all you're going to show her?"

Graham looked at him sharply. As a twenty-year veteran of the force and six months away from retirement, Chambers was beyond intimidation.

He spread his hands wide, still holding the remnants of the candy bar. "You know, she's a beautiful woman, you're a free man." He chuckled. "It's been, how long now since you've been divorced?" He raised and lowered his eyebrows in a poor imitation of a lecher.

Graham waved a hand in dismissal at the man as he turned to leave the squad room. "Eat another burrito, Chambers."

The order evoked a laugh. "Thanks, don't mind if I do."

Graham heard the man's chair squeak as he rose. He had no doubts that Chambers was on his way out to take up his suggestion.

* * *

Caitlin didn't realize until Gray walked through the door late that afternoon that she had been holding her breath all day, waiting for him to return. Afraid that he wouldn't.

Knowing him, she'd half expected Graham to call Jeffers and tell him to take over as the main bodyguard. As it was, the man had been here a great deal longer than she had thought he would be.

Affable, friendly, Ben Jeffers had managed to stay out of her way and yet bring a peaceful tranquillity to the shop. He and Kerry had been sharing a running conversation now for the past hour, interrupted only by the occasional sales that had to be rung up.

Caitlin found herself doing most of the work, which was just as well. Talking to the customers helped keep her mind occupied.

But when she saw Graham walk in, everything came to a screeching halt for her. He was finally back. And she was glad.

She wondered if he was.

Caitlin had no doubts that he cared for her, maybe even still loved her. But with Gray, that wasn't enough. The "right thing" was tied up with his sense of values and his heritage. Doing the "right thing" might not allow him to come to the same conclusion that she had. That they belonged together.

It felt as if there were miles of hurdles in front of her. But she was determined to clear them all. She'd stumbled once and wasted a great deal of her life. She wasn't about to do it again.

Belatedly she realized that the customer beside her had asked her a question. Something to do with deciding which color peignoir to select. She was celebrating her first anniversary Saturday.

It would have been her eleventh next Tuesday if her mother hadn't intervened, Caitlin thought with a pang.

"I'll be just a minute," Caitlin promised the woman. Catching Eva's eye, Caitlin signaled for her to take over.

Eva easily slipped into the spot Caitlin vacated. "Blue,"

she assured the woman as she held the peignoir up against her. "To bring out your eyes."

Caitlin hurried over to Graham, cutting him off from Jeffers. Whatever he had to say to the other man could wait. Kerry could more than keep Jeffers occupied for a few more minutes.

"How did it go?"

He nodded at Jeffers. Since he'd received no calls from his partner, Graham assumed that the time spent here had been uneventful.

He looked at Caitlin. "We think we might have our man." Graham began reaching into his pocket. "I've got a photograph I want you to look at."

She waved it aside for the moment. "I meant with the lawyer."

Why was she concerned about that when her life was still in danger? He frowned at the interruption and the news. "Not so good."

One hand on his arm, she drew Graham to the side. "Why?" she pressed.

He hadn't been prepared for that question. Maybe that was why he answered, he thought. "He said my chances at the outset are less than fifty-fifty."

It was probably worse than that and he just wasn't telling her. She'd hoped that the lawyer would have had some sort of strategy planned.

"There has to be something," she insisted. "Isn't there anything he thought that you could do?"

"Yeah." Graham laughed shortly as he ran a hand over the back of his neck. "Get married between now and the meeting in the judge's chambers." Graham paused as he recalled the wording the lawyer had used. "He said if I could show the court that I could provide a stable life for Jake—for some reason, that means having a wife take care of him instead of just my mother—then the odds would probably lean in my favor, since we're both adoptive parents and Celia did give up custody once."

The lawyer might as well have suggested that he become

an astronaut. Who the hell was he supposed to marry on a moment's notice?

He looked at Caitlin.

For just the tiniest second she thought he was going to say something to her. But then the pregnant moment passed.

Graham dug into his pocket and laid the photograph on the counter. He had to get his mind back on his work and not on his problems. It was making him think ridiculous things.

He tapped a finger at the corner of the photo. "Recognize him?"

Reluctantly she looked down at the photograph. They had been on the edge of something. She had felt sure— But then, when had she ever felt sure with Gray?

Caitlin pressed her lips together, stopping the involuntary gasp that rose in her throat as the face on the photograph penetrated her thoughts. "Oh, God, it's him."

He'd thought so, too, but he had to ask. "Are you sure?"

A white-hot chill sliced through her. She'd seen that face over and over again last night, every time she closed her eyes. Her voice was flat, quiet. "I'm sure."

Graham nodded, slipping the photograph back into his pocket. "We're trying to locate him now. When we do, you're going to have to come down and pick him out of a lineup."

He was making it sound so grim. She tried to smile. "I know. I've watched reruns of *Hill Street Blues*." But knowing what was in store for her didn't make it any easier for her to face. She forced the prospect of what lay ahead from her mind. They'd left the first subject hanging and she wanted to get back to it. "What are you going to do about Jake?"

He'd been going over that in his mind the entire trip from the lawyer's office. The one thing that had suggested itself he had discarded almost immediately. It wouldn't be right. Or fair.

"I don't know. What can I do?" He shoved his hands deep into his pockets. "It's not like I can go to the local super-market and pick out a wife on aisle three."

She was treading on a very thin path and there was quicksand on either side of her. "Not for a lifelong commitment. But you're just looking for a temporary stopgap."

That much was true. He didn't want to enter into any sort of a long-term relationship. Or any relationship at all, for that matter. As far as he was concerned, relationships presented problems and never evolved the way he hoped. He glanced at Caitlin.

At least when he had married Celia he had entered with no illusions. He had expected nothing and had gotten nothing. There had been no disappointments. Not like with Caitlin.

"Yeah," Graham agreed absently, thinking.

His mother's suggestion the other day about returning to the reservation was beginning to have its merits. He and Jake could get lost there—

Graham stopped before the thought took off. There was too much of the cop in him to resort to doing something like that. Running away. Eluding the law. There had to be another way. He frowned.

Maybe…maybe he might be able to enter into an arrangement with one of the women on the reservation—

It was worth a shot.

He turned abruptly on his heel to look at his partner. "Jeffers."

Ben left Kerry hanging midword and crossed to Graham. "Yes?"

"Could you take over detail for me for a couple of days?"

The question caught both Caitlin and the younger detective by surprise.

Jeffers nodded. He saw no problem with that. He was working backup on the case, anyway. "Sure, if the captain doesn't have objections. What's up?"

Caitlin moved closer, coming between the two men. "Yes, what's up?"

She was entirely too close to him, interfering with his concentration. Graham looked over her head to Jeffers. "I was thinking of heading up to the reservation."

Caitlin could read what was on his mind as clearly as if he

had said the words out loud. She felt her heart constricting. "To get married."

It was the first that Ben had heard of the matter, but then, Gray was pretty closemouthed. He stuck his hand out. "Hey, congratulations!"

Graham ignored his partner as he stared at Caitlin. "How did you know?"

Because I know things about you, Gray. I know how your mind works. I know how your heart works.

She kept her thoughts to herself. All but one. "It won't work."

Jeffers looked from one to the other, confused and lost.

She wasn't saying anything that Graham didn't know. He didn't feel good about it, but he had only the one shot and he was desperate. Annoyance shot through him. "Weren't you just urging me to do anything I could to keep Jake, or did I misunderstand that, too?"

She refused to let his anger affect her. "You can't just pick out anyone, Gray," she insisted. "The judge'll see through that. It has to be someone you know." She forced the tension from her voice. She had to make him see reason. "Someone you've had a history with." Her eyes were on his. She saw the resistance. Caitlin went on talking. "So it seems more natural. You could tell him that you're just moving up the date to satisfy the court, that's all."

He didn't respond right away. When he did, his voice was low, foreboding. He didn't want her getting involved in this. "You're talking about you."

"I think you two want to be alone." Jeffers said the words to no one in particular because neither one noticed him. "I'll be at the precinct if you need me." Graham nodded curtly at him. Jeffers said goodbye to Kerry and left.

Caitlin raised her chin stubbornly. "Yes, I'm talking about me."

The woman was crazy. She left him completely speechless. It took a moment to gather his thoughts together.

"Caitlin, I won't accept your money and I won't accept

your lawyer. What the hell makes you even remotely think that I would do something like this?''

Was the idea of marriage to her something so odious to him now? They'd made love last night. Had that simply been a matter of unanswered needs surfacing for him and nothing more?

No, he'd made love to her, made love *with* her because he *loved* her. She refused to believe she had been that wrong. It was just his damn pride getting in the way again.

All right, she'd deal with it in terms he could agree to. ''It's an arrangement, pure and simple. A marriage of convenience, if you will. It's done all the time.''

He'd been willing to do it, but not with someone he cared about. Not with her. He shook his head, rejecting her offer.

Graham saw determination rise in her eyes. She was going to fight him on this.

''And what would the convenience be for you?''

She knew he'd ask. ''I'd be paying off a debt. You did save my life and I don't want to see you lose Jake.'' Though he didn't want to, she could tell he was considering it. Caitlin pressed her advantage. ''We have a history, Gray. It's not as if you just picked me out of a hat or a catalog. The judge won't question it. We were supposed to get married once. I even have the license we took out.''

He looked at her in surprise. ''You kept it?''

Caitlin shrugged. ''Just something I forgot to throw out,'' she lied.

If she was being honest, she wouldn't have been able to say why she kept it. Maybe because when they had signed the papers they'd been so happy, so full of hopes. Throwing it away would have been like throwing that precious memory away.

He studied her face, thinking. Allowing himself to consider the offer, even though it was insane. ''An arrangement?''

''Yes.'' Her expression remained unchanged.

He watched her face, trying to read it. ''And after a respectable amount of time, we'll get divorced?''

Don't you want me, Gray? At least a little? Or are you just being noble? "Yes."

It could work. But then he remembered. There was still a fly in the ointment. A very large, dangerous fly. He couldn't take a chance.

"There's a killer out after you, Caitlin. I can't endanger Jake and my mother like that."

She'd forgotten about that. Forgotten about everything except for this. Caitlin nodded. He was right. She understood.

"It was just an idea." And one that obviously wasn't going to work. She felt frustrated. If he didn't accept this offer, maybe he would reconsider using her lawyer. Or at least allow her to give him a loan. "I wish you'd let me help somehow."

He didn't want her involved. He didn't want her entering any farther into his life than she already was. If she did, he might not let her go when the time came. And she would grow to detest him the way Celia did. The way his mother detested his father. He couldn't bear that with her. "Listening helps."

"Yeah, like you talk." The bell tinkled and she jerked as she turned toward the doorway.

She was still jumpy, he thought. He couldn't blame her. It would probably take her a long time, even after they caught the killer, to learn how to relax again.

And there was a chance they might not catch the killer.

The telephone rang in the back room as Caitlin went to help a customer. Kerry hurried to answer it, leaving a very maternal-looking woman in a delicate quandary between a black teddy and a scarlet one. Graham felt his mouth curving.

The woman caught his eye. Rather than look away or flush, she cocked her head like a starling inspecting a tasty insect. The woman raised her brows and shifted her eyes from one teddy to the other, obviously asking his opinion.

She was old enough to be his mother, if not more.

She was probably younger than he was at this moment, Graham thought, feeling drained and tired.

The woman was still waiting, framed by a teddy in each hand.

"Black," he mouthed.

The woman held the black teddy up higher. Graham nodded and the older woman gleefully bobbed her head in agreement. She discarded the other undergarment, setting it on the counter.

"Miss," she called out to Caitlin. "I've made my decision."

"And a very tasteful one it is," Caitlin agreed, her eyes on Gray. She'd witnessed the exchange. It was sweetly sensitive. Just when she thought she knew him, he surprised her.

"Graham," Kerry called as she walked out of the back room. "There's a phone call for you. It's a Detective Chambers." She held out the receiver to him.

Graham took it and disappeared behind the floral curtain, hoping that Chambers would be less long-winded on the phone than he had been in person that morning.

Chapter 11

Graham pulled aside the curtain less than two minutes later. He looked around for Caitlin and spotted her by the register.

It never ceased to amaze him the way some things seemed to work out. Sometimes a case would drag on forever, taking years to progress, if at all. And sometimes the pieces just fell together with breathtaking speed. Like now. He had learned through hard experience that if a case was going to get anywhere, the first forty-eight hours were always the most crucial.

They had struck pay dirt. It had happened inadvertently, thanks to an overeager reporter who had thrown a witness's safety to the wind for the sake of a story and to a jittery killer who had used the information in an attempt to permanently silence her.

Once he was identified, Horace Taylor's whereabouts were a great deal easier to trace. Not easy, just easier. Networking had been involved. Networking and snitches whose loyalties could be bought for a C-note. And, though he hated to admit it, luck. They had gotten lucky.

Now, if only it lasted.

"Show time," he announced, approaching Caitlin.

Caitlin tore off the middle copy from the charge plate receipt and handed it to the white-haired woman who'd sought Graham's silent fashion advice.

The woman's eyes flickered over Graham. Caitlin had seen that same look before. Women always looked at Graham that way, though he seemed completely oblivious to the fact. The older woman had a wistful smile on her thin lips.

Dreams were free, Caitlin thought, amused, as she turned toward Graham.

Except when you had to pay for them, she reminded herself. She had dreamed of happiness with Graham once. When it hadn't happened, the pain had been almost too much to bear.

"Show time?" Caitlin echoed. She couldn't begin to guess what he was talking about. "Is that some sort of high-tech police jargon?"

The woman at the register was lingering, taking an inordinately long time to tuck her charge plate into her wallet.

"You're a policeman?" Her cornflower blue eyes widened in admiration. "You know, there've been these wild, noisy parties in my neighborhood lately...."

Caitlin expected Graham to briskly brush the woman off. She was surprised when he gave her a tolerant smile. Surprised and pleased.

She looked lively, he thought, and in need of something to feed her obvious zest for life. "Why don't you knock on the door?" he suggested. "And ask if you can join in?"

Her eyes fairly glowed at the prospect. She grinned and Caitlin was struck by how pretty the woman still was. And how lovely she must have once been.

"Thanks, maybe I will." With that, she walked out, holding her package to her and humming.

"Well." Caitlin turned from the doorway to look at Graham. "You certainly brightened up her day. Now, exactly what did you mean by 'show time'?"

The slight curve of his mouth vanished and he looked serious again. Caitlin felt a chill of anticipation creep over her on thin, spiked heels. This had to do with the killer.

Graham looked around. There were only two other customers in the store. There was no reason for Caitlin to have to put this off. No reason except the fear of looking at her would-be killer again.

Compassion filled him, along with the impossible wish that she didn't have to be subjected to this. "Do you feel up to going down to the precinct and trying to pick the suspect out of a lineup?"

She couldn't believe it. "They found the guy? So fast?"

He nodded. "Sometimes fate and the police department work in strange ways."

"Apparently." Something within her hesitated. She'd have to look at the killer. See those ice blue eyes that were filled with hatred and death. Caitlin licked her lips. They felt dry.

"Sure." She took a deep breath. "Why not? The sooner this man goes behind bars, the sooner I'll be able to get my life back."

Exactly what he was thinking. The sooner this was wrapped up, the sooner she could return to her world, and he to his. Worlds that had very little to do with each other.

"Just give me a minute." She moved behind the counter and picked up her purse.

"Bankers' hours, Cait?" Kerry asked, joining her.

"Gray says they've got the guy I saw in the alley in custody." Why was her heart hammering like this? She was going down to the police station. Nothing could hurt her there. And Gray would be with her. "I have to pick him out of a lineup."

Kerry's smile never wavered, but she squeezed Caitlin's hand. There was concern in her eyes. "Be careful, Cait."

"I'm with him." She nodded at Graham, who returned her smile with a quizzical raise of his brow. "What could happen to me?"

Kerry's look of concern melted into a wide smile. For Caitlin's sake she downplayed the possible dangerous repercussions of identifying a killer.

"Lots of things, I hope. And all good." She leaned over

and whispered into Caitlin's ear, "If you need any pointers, just call."

Caitlin laughed. "I'll keep that in mind." Leaving the shelter of her counter, she came around to Graham. "I'm ready." She only hoped that she could live up to those words.

"What was that all about?" He nodded toward Kerry as they walked out of the shop.

"Girl talk." He appeared satisfied with that answer, but because it tickled her, she elaborated. "Kerry thinks I might need a little advice on certain fine points, like how to make love with you."

"You don't need any advice." He circled the hood and got in on the driver's side.

Pleasure curled through her. "Is that a compliment?"

"Just an observation." He glanced in the rearview mirror as he backed the sedan out of the tight spot. "I'm a cop." Graham threw the car into Forward. "That's what I do. Observe."

He was uncomfortable talking about it, about them, so she left the topic alone. Her thoughts returned to what she was about to face. Caitlin's fingertips felt clammy and she folded them into her palms.

"So." Her voice sounded tinny and strained to her ear. "Assuming you have the right man, what happens once I identify him?"

They eased through a light a beat before it turned red. "We arraign him and the case goes down on the calendar for trial."

It sounded so simple. One, two, three and she was safe. Not quite. Caitlin couldn't shake the fear that nibbled at her. "Can he get out on bail?"

Graham knew what she was thinking—that the man would come after her again. "Not for murder."

That meant that she would finally be safe. It also meant other things, she thought, glancing at Graham. Far less pleasing things.

Caitlin blew out a breath, then turned to look at Graham. "That means that I won't need a bodyguard anymore."

"No." Graham kept his eyes on the road.

No. The way he said it, it was almost as if he had said goodbye, as well. She didn't want that to happen. There was still so much ground to regain. Her search for something to hang on to opened another door. "And I won't be being stalked."

Graham glanced at her. Instantly he knew what was going on in her mind. She was thinking about what they had talked about earlier. About why he couldn't agree to a marriage of convenience with her.

"No," he agreed.

He knew what she was inferring. There was a touch of reluctance in his voice, but she chalked it up to Gray's pride. Caitlin nestled back in her seat. Maybe this time fate had dealt them both a winning hand. "Worth thinking about."

He didn't want to think about it, but the court date was breathing down his neck. He had to do something and do it quickly.

In a way, it sounded like the perfect solution. Everything she had said was true. They did have a history together and it would look far less suspicious to the judge if he married her instead of some woman from the reservation. He knew that Celia's lawyer would investigate the situation thoroughly. She was obsessive when she wanted something, and she wanted Jake.

Emotionally, he was leaning toward having his mother arrange for the marriage. He was more than willing to monetarily compensate whoever was chosen. If he married Caitlin, for whatever reasons she professed to agree to, something far greater than money would be involved. He didn't want to go that route *because* his emotions would be involved.

But he didn't want to lose his son, and he knew he would risk anything to keep Jake.

It would be different if he thought that Celia was capable of giving their son what she had boasted that she would. A good, stable home, all the advantages and love. No matter what, parting from Jake would be difficult, but if it was for the boy's own good, he could manage it. Graham knew Celia far too well to be fooled, though.

Oh, for a while Celia would live up to her word, just as she had the last time, when they had adopted Jake. But then the novelty would wear off. She would lose interest and move on to something else. It was a pattern Graham had witnessed more than once. She wouldn't do it to be spiteful or cruel. But Jake would be the one to suffer.

That couldn't be allowed to happen.

The room was small, windowless and dim. One side of it was glass, looking out onto another, larger room, just as windowless, just as grimly foreboding.

Caitlin braced herself.

"There's nothing to be afraid of," Graham murmured quietly as he ushered her in.

His eyes were kind, reassuring. Caitlin tried to relax. She couldn't.

There was another policeman in the room with them to witness the proceedings. She hardly noticed. Her eyes were on the small stagelike area in the other room where eight men would be brought in for her to view.

Eight men, and one of them would be the killer. A man who had wanted to kill her.

Her shoulders were stiff enough to use as a diving board. Graham shifted so that she was forced to look at him. "They can't see you."

"But he'll know," Caitlin said quietly as a young policeman herded a group of men into the room and toward the backlit stage.

There was no getting away from that. "Yeah, he'll know."

Taking a deep breath, Caitlin watched as one by one the men, wearing consecutive numbers around their necks, lined up in order. They were told to face front and stand up straight.

They were all more or less the same height, the same weight. They appeared to vary by approximately ten, maybe fifteen years in age. The idea was to have her dig deep into her soul before she made her identification.

Forcing herself to study the men one at a time instead of

scanning the group, Caitlin looked carefully from one man to the next.

When she looked at number six, the air stagnated in her lungs. After what seemed like an eternity, Caitlin continued.

Graham saw the way she had hesitated. "Take your time, Caitlin. Don't rush."

He'd recognized the man instantly. But they needed her ID as well as his to corroborate.

She didn't want to take her time, she wanted to be out of there. Now. As far away from the man on the other side of the one-way glass as possible.

But she looked at the last two men, then returned to number six. The man whom she knew beyond the shadow of a doubt was the killer.

"Number six." Her voice quavered and she cleared her throat. "Number six," she repeated.

Graham gave no indication that he agreed or disagreed with her. This was her call. "You're sure?"

She nodded her head, her eyes riveted on the man wearing a placard with the number six around his neck. Horace Taylor stared toward the mirrored glass as if he knew exactly where she was standing. Where she was looking. It was hard for her not to flinch. "I'm sure."

Graham nodded. Leaning over to a speaker that was connected directly to the other room, he flipped a switch, turning it on.

"Take number six down and book him," he instructed the policeman on the other side of the glass. "Tell the others they can go." He flipped the switch into the Off position before looking at Caitlin again. "Are you all right?"

She nodded. Number six was glaring directly at her, though she knew he saw only his own reflection. Malevolence emanated from him as he was led off. He didn't act like a man who was afraid of what was in store for him. He looked like a man planning his revenge.

"Who is he?"

She looked unsteady on her feet. Graham instinctively took hold of her arm. "A lowlife who won't bother you again."

Caitlin pulled her arm away. She wanted to know the truth. "Don't wrap tissue paper around me, Gray. I'm a big girl. A big girl who was almost kidnapped yesterday by some crazy man who would have killed me as easily as he would have spit on the sidewalk. Now, who is he?"

Graham paused, exchanging looks with the policeman in the room. The other man understood the unspoken message and left the room. Graham folded his arms before him as he leaned a hip against the small table that housed the speaker and looked at Caitlin. He didn't want her dirtied by the slime that existed in the world he dealt with. But she already had been.

"His name is Horace Taylor." Methodically he gave Caitlin a rundown of the man's priors. They were extensive and made her flesh creep.

"He's also suspected of fingering his former boss for a hit," Graham concluded. "He's entrenched with some new group in Phoenix. A drug cartel. He's added that to his list of connections."

There was always a new group, he thought, and it was always the same. The new wiped out the old and made the same mistakes. The only difference was that it always seemed to get uglier.

Caitlin was trying her damnedest to look unfazed, but he could see that she was shaken. "Do you want me to take you home?" he asked.

She wasn't a hothouse orchid that fell apart at the slightest thing, but this was a little bit too real for her to assimilate in a few minutes. It was almost time to close up shop, anyway.

She nodded. "Yes." And then she smiled. "Kerry is going to think that this is becoming a habit."

His hand on her shoulder, he guided her to the door. "Doesn't the boss lady get to kick back?"

"Not if she wants to continue being the boss of something." Caitlin walked through the doorway and waited for him to join her. "Bosses work harder than anyone. They have to."

She glanced at the closed door of the other room, the one Taylor had just been in.

"Don't think about it," Graham told her. "It's over."

But they both knew it wasn't. Not really. There was still the trial to face.

In the parking lot Caitlin walked over to the dark sedan, ready to get in. But Graham took her arm and nodded at the pink Cadillac convertible parked beside it. She looked at him quizzically.

"That's the department's car," he reminded her, indicating the sedan. "This one's mine. With Taylor behind bars, I'm not on bodyguard detail anymore. I'm on my own time now."

His own time. And how much of that would she get to share with him? Questions multiplied in her mind as she got into the car. Caitlin wanted to press, to ask him, now that this stumbling block was out of the way, what he thought of her suggestion.

But there was only so far she could push. Any more and Graham would back away. The terrain was more unsteady this time around than the last.

He said nothing as he pulled out of the lot. His mind struggled with his conscience. He had meant everything he'd said earlier about believing that things had turned out for the best. Marriage just wouldn't have worked out for them. He'd found out the hard way that he just wasn't husband material. He hadn't been able to make his marriage last, even for Jake's sake. Added to that was the clash between their backgrounds. He had found that he didn't blend in at the reservation or the all-white high school he had attended. Always odd man out. He didn't want to subject Caitlin to that sort of life. They might have had a past, but there wasn't going to be a future for them.

It just wouldn't work.

He was thinking of marriage in terms of what he had wanted once. But it didn't have to work that way now. It didn't have to work at all, something whispered. It just had to be. For a given time period.

Just long enough to get permanent custody of Jake. However long that might take.

His lawyer had looked at him grimly after reviewing the pages in Jake's folder and said that judges tended to rule in favor of the mother. By his own admission, Graham had told the lawyer that Celia had never physically abused Jake, she had just neglected him. But there had been nothing criminal about it because he had been there to pick up the slack. It could be effectively argued that she had known that and indulged herself without any harm coming to the boy.

Now his ex-wife had returned to the scene professing to be a changed woman. Certainly her marital status and her financial situation had changed, putting her one up on Graham, who had neither a spouse nor a healthy bank account to point to.

The lawyer hadn't pulled any punches. The scales would be tipped in Celia's direction.

He had to tip them back in his favor. Graham searched for the right words. The words that would somehow make this all right, even when he knew in his heart that it wasn't. "Caitlin, I know it's been a rough day for you...."

The air that whizzed by them as they drove was hot. She felt as if her eyelashes were sweating. But, damp eyelashes not withstanding, it was great to be alive. She turned, smiling. "Compared to yesterday at this time, this is a cakewalk."

He nodded, falling into silence again. *Bad idea. You've got to find another way.*

"You were going to ask me something?" she prompted. Unable to take the heat, she lifted her hair up from her neck.

"I changed my mind," he muttered.

So near and yet so far. Caitlin dropped her hair again. "I know talking isn't easy for you...."

He'd always been more comfortable in silence. If things weren't said, they didn't have to be taken back. "You always knew how to take up the slack."

"Flatterer." She could see that the words were there, on his tongue. He just couldn't make himself say them. "Okay, do you want me to take up the slack this time?"

Yes. No. Damn, there was no simple way to go in this. "If it comes with subtitles."

Eleven years ago he had slipped a ring on her finger. He hadn't asked then, either, she remembered. Words were not a medium he dealt in comfortably. It had just been understood. All right, she'd help him out.

"It's a very modern age we're living in, Gray. There are a lot of arrangements being made these days that wouldn't have been tolerated fifteen, twenty years ago."

He glanced at her, silent, waiting for her to get to the point.

"There are women who, for a fee, will allow themselves to be used as surrogate mothers."

Was she being serious? Did she really mean that she would be willing to view this as just an arrangement, nothing more? It was a great deal to ask. But it couldn't be done any other way.

"Go on," he said evenly.

She continued, feeling her way along a rocky terrain with only bravado to guide her. "Most of the time they do it for perfect strangers. Your situation right now is kind of like that." Caitlin rushed through the rest of it, afraid he would interrupt her and she would lose momentum. "You need a surrogate mother for Jake in order to please the court. I'd like to do that for you."

She'd turned it around, away from the two of them and toward Jake. But then, he thought, she'd always been clever.

He eased his foot off the gas pedal as the light up ahead changed from green to yellow. "You'd really find that agreeable? To marry me for Jake's sake and then later get a divorce?"

She smiled, though it was tinged in sadness. "I haven't said 'I do' yet and you're already having me say 'I don't.'"

He thought that they'd already been through that part of it. "Caitlin, I'm not going to ask you to marry me in any real sense of the word. I don't have anything to offer you."

She knew getting into a discussion over this was futile. But if she didn't tell him this, he wouldn't understand any of it. "I'm not asking for anything, Gray." *I just want you.*

No, she hadn't asked. That didn't mean she shouldn't have. They were just too different. And he was empty inside, except for the love he had for his son. This wasn't going to work, he thought. Not on any level.

"But I am asking," he said firmly. "For you. Your mother would make your life a living hell if you married me."

She would handle her mother. She was looking forward to it. "Let me worry about my mother, Gray. After what she's done, she isn't exactly welcome in my life, anyway."

There were more reasons against this, darker reasons. He'd seen what had happened when his father had been with his mother. How love had quickly dried up and turned into something empty. Something ugly. How even with an understanding, his own marriage had fallen apart. Caitlin had never lived through that kind of experience. And he couldn't let her do that for him.

Graham shook his head. "I can't ask you to marry me, Caitlin," he repeated.

Caitlin pushed past the pain his words created. There was a small boy to think of. One she was certain needed Graham's love. Perhaps even as much as she did.

"All right. Can you ask me to be Jake's mother?" From the corner of her eye she saw Graham turn his head to look at her. She kept her eyes straight ahead, afraid that she might lose her nerve if she looked at him. "The other will be a technicality, like a form you have to sign."

She seemed determined, despite everything he said. "Why are you doing this?"

If he had to ask, maybe he really didn't know her at all. "Because you love him and I don't want to see you hurt. I don't want to see Jake hurt. I don't know Celia, but she doesn't sound like my idea for a candidate for mother of the year." When he said nothing, she looked at him. "I've heard you on the phone with Jake, seen the look in your eyes when you mention him. You've finally found someone to love, someone who loves you back, and I want you to have that."

She took a breath, steeling herself. "Maybe what we had is gone." In her heart she refused to believe it. But he did, and for now, she let it stand. "But what you and Jake have is alive and thriving. A boy needs his father. He needs someone who's willing to do anything for him. That's love."

"But your life—"

She wasn't going to let him talk her out of it. "I'm not making that big a sacrifice. I'm still going on with my life. Besides," she said, a cryptic smile curving her mouth, "there's an added bonus."

"Which is?"

She shifted in her seat to face him. "I get to tell my mother about it." Caitlin's smile broadened. "After the fact."

Graham laughed softly under his breath. "I never thought you could be spiteful."

She was serious as she answered him. "Neither did I."

Caitlin studied Graham's profile for a long moment. She didn't know whether she had convinced him or not. He should be the one convincing her, she thought, frustrated. This was his son. Why were favors so hard for him to accept? Why was his pride always such an obstacle?

"So, what do you think? For Jake?"

There was no way he could refuse the offer, not if it meant keeping his son. Jake had gone through enough when Celia had left them. He had been convinced that it was his fault his mother had walked out. It had taken a great deal of assurance from Graham to make him believe otherwise.

And now Jake's world could be torn apart again. With the possibility of more upheavals in the future, should Celia change her mind.

When Celia changed her mind, Graham amended.

Graham pulled up in front of Caitlin's house. He realized that she was holding her hand out to him, waiting to seal a bargain. The hand was like a lifeline to a drowning man.

He had no choice, though he wished he did. For her sake.

"For Jake." He nodded. "You've got a deal." He slipped his hand into hers. "Hell of a way to propose to a woman," he muttered, shaking his head.

She lifted a shoulder and let it drop, feigning nonchalance. "Yeah, well, you did a little better the first time around."

"I was naive," he countered.

Her smile was sad, though she fought against it. "There's something to be said for that." But for now, there were other things to concentrate on. She was going to get married.

To a man who was marrying her only because he had to.

Chapter 12

Caitlin hadn't pictured it this way.

When she had thought of her wedding, she had never pictured it like this. Standing in front of a sleepy-eyed, scrawny-looking justice of the peace, his thin face pockmarked with white stubble like tiny white shoots pushing their way out of a cracked, creased earth. His wife, a big-boned, pleasant-faced woman, hovered in attendance, acting as a witness.

And Graham.

Graham belonged in the fantasy, but not like this. Not standing beside her so solemn that he looked as if he were attending a funeral instead of a wedding. His wedding. Their wedding.

Tired pink plastic roses drooped from vases strategically set around a living room crammed with knickknacks. "The Wedding March" floated weakly out of a music box that appeared older than she was. Everything needed dusting.

There were no friends to wish them well, nothing about this ceremony to differentiate it from the thousands of others that had come before. And the thousands of others that would come after.

Nothing, she reminded herself, clutching the plastic bouquet that the justice of the peace's wife had shoved into her hands at the last moment, except the two of them. *That* made the difference.

They had arrived at the last-minute decision in her driveway. Graham had taken the only chance he had of keeping Jake. He had agreed that they should drive to Las Vegas and get married. Quickly, before common sense stepped in and forbade him to go through with it.

They had paused only long enough for Graham to call his mother from Caitlin's house. And then only to inform Lily that he wouldn't be home that night. He didn't say a word about getting married.

Caitlin, overhearing the conversation and what wasn't said, tried not to let it bother her.

His mother had told him that Celia had come over and tried to see the boy. Jake had been playing at a friend's house and Lily had turned her away.

If Graham had had any lingering doubts about going through with the wedding, that had made up his mind for him. His back was to the wall.

So they had driven the three hundred miles that stretched between Phoenix and Las Vegas, stopping only long enough to get gas and pick up hamburgers, sodas and fries.

Her prenuptial supper, Caitlin had thought wryly, holding Graham's container of fries up for him so he could eat and drive at the same time. It might make for an interesting story someday. If they had a someday together.

Six and a half hours later, at ten-thirty at night, exhausted, wired and dusty, with a freshly inked license issued by the all-night marriage license bureau on Third Street, Graham had woken up Justice of the Peace Henry Richards at The True Love Chapel and asked the elderly man to perform the wedding ceremony.

Caitlin's stomach was tied up in knots, but she couldn't stop smiling. Not even when Flora Richards had shuffled out in a hot pink robe that had several long threads hanging from the hem, pushed the plastic roses into her hands and produced a veil, of all things, for her to wear.

She was marrying Graham.

At two minutes to eleven, with the required fee tucked into the pocket of his nubby peacock blue bathrobe, Henry Richards was sleepily murmuring the appropriate words over them.

"The ring, please." Looking at Graham, Henry stifled a yawn.

Graham looked at Caitlin, taken aback. They had driven here so quickly he had completely forgotten about getting a ring.

"Don't you have a ring, dear?" Flora asked kindly. Sympathy was etched into her face. Not waiting for an answer, she tugged off a thin band from her pinkie, struggling to get it free.

"It's a friendship ring." She laughed, offering it to Graham. "It's only costume jewelry, but in a pinch, until you can get her a real one…"

Her voice trailed off, melting into the smile on her lips. Flora Richards had witnessed over five thousand ceremonies performed during her own marriage. In all that time she couldn't remember ever seeing a more radiant-looking bride than the one standing here beside her somber groom.

More than five thousand ceremonies, and each and every time the scene left her misty-eyed. She dabbed at her eyes with the corner of her sleeve as she held the ring up for Graham.

Embarrassed, Graham accepted the ring with a murmured thanks. He felt for his wallet with his other hand. "How much do I owe you?"

Flora's hand closed over his, pushing it away. "Nothing, dear. Keep it. For luck," she said softly. Her eyes shifted to the young woman standing beside him. *You two are going to need it.*

Henry yawned again, thinking longingly of his bed. "All right." He sliced through the air with a long, skinny index finger. "Slip the ring on her finger and repeat after me. With this ring, I thee wed."

I'm sorry, Caitlin. I'm really sorry. Graham's eyes held hers as he echoed the words. "With this ring, I thee wed."

Yes, Gray. Yes, you do. She pressed her lips together to keep the tears back. Now everything was up to her.

Henry smiled. This was the part he always liked. "By the power vested in me by the state of Nevada, I now pronounce you husband and wife." He closed the thick black bound book and removed his glasses. "You may kiss the bride."

"Well, go on," Flora urged when Graham made no move to follow Henry's instruction. "Nothing to be embarrassed about. We've seen kissing before." She chuckled. "Had one couple here about a month ago that looked as if they were going to start their honeymoon right here in our living room. Practically had to turn a hose on them."

She sighed and Caitlin had the definite impression that Flora wouldn't have minded all that much if they had begun their marriage right there.

Because the woman didn't look as if she was going to let them go until he complied, Graham raised Caitlin's veil and brushed his lips quickly over hers.

Flora looked displeased. "Better do better than that if you don't want to avail yourself of Henry's other package deal." Caitlin raised a brow in silent question. "He also does divorces, though we don't like to broadcast the fact," she confided as she took back her bouquet and veil from Caitlin. "Puts a damper on the ceremony."

But that was exactly where the ceremony would lead, Caitlin thought. It was only a matter of time. A divorce was what was waiting for her at the end. It was what she had agreed to and what would happen, unless something changed it.

Flora clutched her husband's arm and all but dragged him along as she accompanied Caitlin and Graham to the front door. "Have a wonderful life," Flora urged, calling after them as they left. "Be very, very happy."

"She sounds as if she really means that," Graham muttered, walking down the steep front steps to the sidewalk.

"Maybe she does." Caitlin stopped at the passenger side

of Graham's car. Their car, she amended silently. At least for now. "Maybe she just loves watching weddings."

He laughed under his breath as he opened the door for her. "Even tacky ones?"

Caitlin smiled. The wedding wasn't the last word in elegance, but it was still precious to her. "Even tacky ones."

She settled in beside Graham in the huge pink vehicle. Somehow, between now and then, whenever "then" might be, she was going to have to convince him that their marriage would work.

How, she hadn't the slightest idea.

In any event, they had their work cut out for them. There was still the hearing in the judge's chambers. And at least a year of being husband and wife after that. Plenty of time to convince Gray that he couldn't live without her.

She turned and looked at him, wondering what he was thinking. They were still sitting parked at the curb before the bright pink sign that proclaimed the chapel's name along with the number of ceremonies performed there.

And now they would be among the number, Caitlin mused. "Where to now?"

He placed the key into the ignition and paused before turning it on. He tried not to think about what he had just done. "Home."

She stared. "Gray, it's after eleven o'clock. It's not as if you can just click your heels, mutter 'There's no place like home' and get there."

She could see by his expression that he wasn't following her. He was probably the only living human being who'd never seen *The Wizard of Oz* or believed in places existing over the rainbow at least once in his life.

She tried again. "Home is another six-hour drive. You're exhausted. Why don't we just get a room for the night and get an early start in the morning?"

He didn't want to stay here in some small hotel room with her. With Caitlin filling up every available space. Once it wouldn't have mattered. Once he had loved her enough to block out things like reason. But now he was too aware of life's realities. Of its pitfalls. And consequences.

He had married her for one reason only. He had to remember that.

He was tired, drained. Being alone with her would not be wise. Defenses that needed to be up, against her, against himself, were dangerously undermanned and weak. If he wasn't careful, he was going to get entangled again.

But, much as he hated to admit it, she was making sense. He was exhausted. Driving three hundred miles back to Phoenix didn't exactly entice him.

She did. Whether he was tired or not, Caitlin enticed him.

Graham squared his shoulders. He'd just have to work on it, that was all. He was an adult, fully capable of controlling his emotions.

He nodded, starting the car. "All right. We'll stay the night."

Round one to the paleface in the corner. Caitlin sat back against the seat. "You're making it sound like a jail sentence." Humor curved her mouth.

Graham made no reply.

Caitlin settled into the silence. She felt excited, wired and fatigued all at the same time. She had lost her virginity to a man she'd always loved, nailed a killer and gotten married in the living room of a house that was a pink nightmare and the last word in clutter. Not bad for twenty-four hours' work.

She wasn't talking, Graham noticed. That was odd for Cait. Was it because she was already regretting her rash action? She knew that this was only temporary, he reminded himself. And he'd find a way to make it up to her. That much he swore.

Driving down the outskirts of the strip, he saw a lit vacancy sign. It was in front of a collection of rooms that were joined together like a pop-bead necklace carelessly tossed down in the desert.

"How's this?" he asked mechanically.

She wondered if they changed the sheets here regularly and

how bad the insect infestation was. "It's a room," she answered brightly. "It'll do fine."

No, it wouldn't. Not for her. He could stay here—he was accustomed to places like this. She wasn't.

He began to drive past the motel. The classier hotels were farther up on the strip. "We could drive to the Excalibur, or—"

Caitlin shook her head. This seemed good enough to him or he wouldn't have asked. That was all that mattered. She didn't want him to feel that she required anything more than he did.

"This is fine, Gray." She placed her hand over his. "Really."

It was only for the night. What difference did it make? He was suddenly too tired to debate this with her, as well. Graham parked the car in front of the manager's office and got out. Caitlin hurried out of the car to catch up.

There was a balding man in an I Love Las Vegas T-shirt sitting behind the front desk, halfheartedly watching the portable television set beside him. He came to life as the front door creaked, announcing their entrance.

Rising, he smiled broadly. "Interest you folks in a room?"

Graham was about to ask for two rooms, but stopped himself. They were married now, if in name only. He might as well start acting like it. "Yes."

The slight man pulled out a ledger from behind the desk and placed it in front of Graham. "Planning on staying here long?"

Graham looked around. The manager's office had a grimy look to it, though it was basically clean. "Just the night."

Deep-set eyes slid down as much of Caitlin's torso as was visible from his position. An appreciative light entered the manager's eyes. "Yeah, I know how that is."

"No," Graham said evenly, his voice low, dangerous. "You don't." She didn't belong in a place like this, where she was visually undressed by some degenerate running a third-rate motel. He should have followed his instincts and driven to a real hotel.

His nerves were on edge. Caitlin leaned over and placed her hand on his arm soothingly as she looked at the manager.

"We just got married. At The True Love Chapel." She raised her left hand and the ring shifted slightly.

The manager's face immediately sobered. "Oh, well, I'm sorry. I didn't mean to—" He looked nervously at Graham, apparently not knowing what to expect. "I don't have a bridal suite, but I can give you the best room I do have."

He turned and selected a key from the board behind him. Showing it to Graham, he laid the key on the desk beside the ledger.

"Number twelve." He leaned over the desk, looking out into the inky darkness just beyond the screened door. The man pointed off into the distance. "It's right at the end of the row."

"Thanks." Graham closed his hand over the key. He wrote his name down, then paused and appended "and wife" to the signature. Charade or not, this was going to take some getting used to.

Standing on her toes, Caitlin leaned over his shoulder and looked at the two words he had added. She grinned. Typical.

"Do you want me to walk ten paces behind you?" she teased.

Graham shrugged, uneasy. "Look, I'm just not used to—"

"Neither am I," she said softly, her eyes touching his. *It won't be easy, but we can do this, Gray. We can,* she pledged silently. She wanted to be out of the manager's office and alone with him. She hooked her arm through his. "Let's go."

It was nicer than she had expected, though everything inside the room was worn, faded by the constant intrusion of the merciless desert sun. It was just large enough for the two of them, with a tiny bathroom off to the side. The drapes were open, and a midnight view of the desert lay just beyond.

It could be romantic, she thought. With the right person.

The room felt oddly quiet as Graham closed the door behind her. Caitlin fingered her new ring. It wobbled. She was going to have to wrap a bit of tape around the back of the band if she didn't want it to fall off.

He saw her twisting the band about her finger. "Sorry about the ring."

She merely smiled. "It's lovely." Everything was lovely. She was Mrs. Graham Redhawk and had a son. Life was wonderful.

He shoved his hands into his back pockets. A few minutes ago he'd felt exhausted. Now he was restless. "I'll get you a real ring when we get back. I can at least do that much."

"If you want." She held up her hand and looked at the two clasped hands depicted on the band. "I really do like this one."

He didn't see how that was possible, but he wasn't going to argue with her. He'd pick up a decent ring when he got the chance. Right now he needed to get some sleep.

The room felt small, like a pair of shoes that didn't fit. He nodded his head toward a straight-back chair with minimal padding on it. The floral pattern was terribly faded, like the comforter and the drapes.

"I'll sleep on the chair."

"Why? The bed's big enough for both of us." The mattress didn't even sag in the middle, she noted silently with a smile.

He dragged a hand through his hair. He was trying to be noble about this and she was making it damn hard on him. "Cait, this is an arrangement, remember?"

His tone drove her smile away. "Yes, but the arrangement doesn't call for solitary confinement or hard time." She fisted her hands at her waist as she pointedly looked him up and down. "You're too big to stretch out comfortably in that chair."

He wasn't thinking of comfort. Comfort would have meant not having Caitlin in the room at all. "I'll manage."

"But I won't." She wouldn't be able to sleep, knowing he was sitting up in the chair like some early-Christian penitent. Her eyes flashed as she looked up at him. "If you don't want to come near me, that's fine." She turned away from the bed, away from him. "I'll take the damn chair." Grabbing a pillow from the bed, she threw it on the chair. "I'm smaller."

"Cait—" Graham grabbed her by the shoulders as she pushed past him.

She jerked her head up and there were tears in her eyes when she looked at him. "What?"

Damn, he'd hurt her. Again. He didn't want to make her cry. He just wanted to make this as easy as he could for both of them.

But when she looked up at him like that, her eyes shimmering with tears that he was responsible for, something tore inside him.

Madness intruded, urging him on to do what he had no business doing. Madness. That was the only explanation there could be for how he had gone from holding her at arm's length to holding her against him, to kissing her, molding her body until it was sealed to his.

And once he kissed her, there could be no turning back.

A multitude of emotions spilled out, melding, blending, until they were all one and the same to him. And they were all her.

Hunger for her, for what he had sampled with her, burned away his reason, his common sense. Hunger urged him on, like a devil whispering in his ear. His hands passed over her body urgently. The very feel of her body made him almost lose his mind.

He wanted to rip away her clothes so that he could feel her—warm, supple, inviting. Graham hardly recognized himself.

Yes, it was madness. And the madness had a name. Caitlin.

Thank you. It was the last truly coherent thought that Caitlin had as joy filled her, then spilled into oblivion as something stronger, something fiercer seized her.

Her breathing ragged, she returned kiss for kiss, touch for touch, urgency for urgency. She was as eager as he for the wondrous, cleansing rush that lovemaking brought. It was as if she'd been holding her breath since last night, waiting for this moment, unsure that it would ever come. Desperately glad when it did. Knowing she would have died if it didn't.

If his hands were zealous in their quest, hers were more so.

If he was impatient to taste her, to touch her, she was more impatient to taste him, to touch him. To feel him, to have him feel her. She wanted desperately to become lost in that incredible inferno of needs and fulfillments, of satisfaction and insatiability.

Her fingers flew over his shirt, pushing buttons through their holes, yanking away at the material until it finally left his torso free. Her own blouse hung open, the clasp in the front of her bra undone so that the two cups just barely hugged her breasts.

His hands found her, covered her, making her moan as the rough calluses on his palms rubbed against the sensitive skin.

Loving her. Worshiping her.

He should have more strength than this. But he didn't. He knew he should be pulling away. But he couldn't. She made him as weak as a kitten, as supplicant as a petitioner begging for forgiveness.

For a crust of bread.

For one sample of her mouth.

He felt like one of his mother's sand drawings, about to be blown away in the wind if he couldn't have Caitlin, if he couldn't possess her just one more time.

She came so willingly it sparked his guilt, but then the next moment guilt was burned away in the heat of his desire.

Graham knew what he had said to her, what he had meant. This was an arrangement and she wasn't to be hurt by it. But something within him would die if he couldn't have her now.

Anticipation throbbed within her, drumming a lyrical rhythm that only he could match. She undid his trousers as he unhooked her skirt, their hands questing for secrets they were already beginning to learn. Clothing fell to the floor, discarded, joined by underwear lost in a flurry of expectation.

Each sought anxiously, fervently, for that elusive something they knew was missing.

Naked, wanting, they wound around each other, cleaving, forming something neither thought the other was aware of.

A whole.

The bed creaked and groaned beneath their combined

weight. They hardly noticed. The fire was consuming them. Holding her hands beneath his spread palms, Graham dressed Caitlin in a wreath of openmouthed kisses that propelled her to a height that took her breath away.

Perspiration glowed along her body as she twisted and turned, eager to welcome him in her, eager to have the fireworks explode.

Wanting this to go on forever.

She gasped as his mouth moved from hers, trailing along her body again, this time forging lower. Spasms seized her, making the skin along her belly quiver as he flicked his tongue along it.

"Gray—"

"Shh." The word, the single sound, whispered like a fiery brand along her flesh. She felt something building, a crescendo that begged for a release, one final loud note to sound as it echoed into the night.

His mouth found her, the soft inner core that welcomed him. Begged for him. He dived his tongue in and she bit her lip, her nails scrambling along the comforter, bunching it, snagging it.

It built higher, higher, then exploded in her veins, pulling her into a vortex.

She wanted more.

She wanted it to stop.

She didn't want to experience this alone. "Gray," she cried, wanting him now.

It shouldn't be this way, he thought. It wasn't supposed to be like this. And yet, it couldn't be any other way. He hadn't the strength to hold back. Not when it was her beneath him like this. She did things to him that no other woman did.

She made him lose his control.

She was fresh, like the pure snow, a blank sheet of paper for him to write on. He'd been her first. It was humbling. Graham wanted to give her the moon and the stars. He wanted to give her everything she deserved, everything she warranted.

All he had was himself.

He moved up along her body. Caitlin twisted beneath him,

sending the flame within him up so high it rivaled the lights that blazed a short distance away along the strip.

''Gray?'' Her voice was all but begging him to enter. To run to the crest with her. It was there, just up ahead. She didn't want to reach it alone.

Unable to deny her any longer, to deny himself any longer, Graham entered her. Caitlin arched her hips high, winding her legs around him, making him drive in deep.

Her cry was muffled against his mouth as he covered hers. He didn't know if it was a cry of protest or ecstasy.

Or even, really, if it was her cry or his. It was all one and the same. A glorious same, as they were joined as one.

Filling her, sheathed in her, Graham began to move more urgently. He framed her face with his hands, his mouth on hers. Drinking in her sweetness. Offering her what he could of himself.

The ride was wild, urgent. They took it together, two orphans in a storm, skimming the river rapids in a skiff made of dreams that once were.

The heat swallowed them both up until it melded with the dim lamplight and then slowly disappeared into the night.

The only sound that remained in the room was the sound of their breathing.

Chapter 13

Her fingers curled along the coarse sheet, reaching for him. There was nothing there but more sheet.

Caitlin opened her eyes. The space beside her on the bed was empty, just as it had been when she'd woken up yesterday. Her heart thudded against her rib cage. Had he left?

The next moment a noise in the room caught her attention. Graham was there, at the window. Completely dressed.

Caitlin sighed. Sitting up, she pulled the sheet around her and dragged her hand through her hair. There was a mist of sleep still enshrouding her brain, but even so, she could see that things had reverted back to where they had been just before she and Graham had entered this room.

It was there, in his eyes, when he turned to look at her.

She glanced at her watch. It was still early, but he was obviously anxious to get going. She smiled, stretching. "Why didn't you wake me?"

Graham tucked his shirt into the waistband of his jeans. His long dark hair hung about his face, damp from the shower. He'd slipped out of bed earlier, careful not to wake her. If she'd held out her arms to him, sleep still heavy on her lids, he knew he couldn't have resisted her.

And he was going to have to learn how. Having her stretch like that in front of him wasn't helping any.

"I liked watching you sleep." He pushed his hair back, out of his eyes. "Besides, only one of us can use the shower at a time."

That's what you think. Caitlin smiled dreamily to herself. There was a great deal of work ahead of her. But she was up to it. As long as she didn't lose sight of the goal.

Her smile filled out the crevices of his soul. "We could have tried to make it fit."

Her comment created an image in his mind he'd have been better off without. Graham had spent half the night awake, watching her, remembering the way things had once been. The way he had once dreamed things could be. The way he now knew they couldn't.

He'd spent the rest of the time attempting to get his feelings under control.

He couldn't do it if she looked as fresh as morning dew on a prairie flower. And he couldn't do it if he kept giving in to himself, the way he had last night.

Graham longed to cross to her, to take her into his arms and kiss her until her lips were bruised from the imprint of his. Keeping the length of the room between them was the only safe way to go, so he remained where he was, his hands in his pockets.

Another mistake he'd made without meaning to. "Cait, I'm sorry."

Without moving a muscle, she stiffened. "Why? About what?"

Why was she making him spell it out for her? She knew what he was trying to say. Graham paused, then began again. "Last night…"

She looked at him sharply. *Don't take away my dreams, Gray.*

The smile remained on her lips, but it fell short of her eyes.

"Last night you did everything just right." The smile hardened just a shade. "There's nothing to be sorry for."

They couldn't keep waltzing around like this. "Cait, if this is going to work—"

She didn't want to hear it. Elaborately she looked at her watch. "Heavens, look at the time." Caitlin swung her legs over the side of the bed, pulling the sheet with her. "I'd better take that shower if we're going to get going."

Rising, she tucked the sheet around her. Caitlin struggled to keep her emotions from showing as she hurried to the next room before Graham could complete his sentence.

She let go of the sheet and it pooled to the dingy vinyl floor as she moved the shower curtain back. Everything was still wet, still fresh with his scent. Caitlin stepped into the tub, pulling the slick curtain closed again.

She felt isolated, alone.

Picking up the soap, she held it up to her face and inhaled. If she tried, she could just faintly detect his scent. Or maybe that was just her imagination.

"Oh, Gray, why won't you try to let it work?" she whispered to herself. "Why do you have to fight it so hard? I was in your heart once. Let me back in."

Taking a deep breath, she turned the shower dial and let the cold water hit her. Maybe the force of the spray would make her feel better somehow, more capable of facing up to the challenge before her.

She began scrubbing furiously, trying to rid herself of the dejected feeling that threatened to overtake her. Her skin stung, growing pink. It helped, a little.

Turning beneath the shower head, she began to smile again. Nothing could scrub away the way his hands had felt along her body last night. And no matter what happened, nothing would ever change that.

She was ready within fifteen minutes. They checked out and then stopped at a drive-through for breakfast. She'd heard him on the telephone earlier, talking to Jeffers while she was still in the bathroom. Did that have anything to do with his quick exodus?

Or was it just that he couldn't wait to be out of here, away from the scene of their wedding? Away from the intimacy they had shared?

She pushed the thought from her mind and slowly ate her wedding breakfast. A muffin with a fried egg and a piece of Canadian bacon nestled inside it. She sipped her coffee as miles of nothing stretched before them.

They were married and that was all that counted for now.

They reentered Phoenix six hours later. Barely half a dozen sentences had passed between them during the trip. Caitlin attributed it to the fact that, Graham being Graham, he was working all this out in his head slowly. There could be no intrusion during this mental duel, so she left him to his thoughts. Rather than conversation, country and western music from the radio filled the empty space.

Her mouth curved. She could relate to the mournful tales of woe that came wafting across the airwaves. Some golden-throated woman was declaring that she couldn't make love with her lover's body if his heart and soul weren't in it.

Tell me about it, Caitlin thought sadly as she glanced at Graham's rigid profile.

Sighing inwardly, she looked out the side window. The route was beginning to look much too familiar.

"Gray, where are we going?" Did he live that close to her? All this time and she hadn't known? It didn't seem possible.

"Home."

He wasn't talking about his own home. She could tell from his tone. Did he think he could just bring her back and then leave, as if she were some book he'd checked out of the library for the day and then returned after he'd got his information?

"This is the way to my house."

"Yes, I know."

She probably wanted to go home to change, Graham felt, to be in her own surroundings for a while. None of what had happened in the past twenty-four hours had exactly been planned. He thought that perhaps she wanted a little time to herself to get her bearings and come to grips with what she'd done.

He knew that he did.

Caitlin shook her head. "'Home' means your house now." She stopped, unsure of what to say next. Why was talking to him so difficult now? It had always been so easy for her. Even though they'd come from different backgrounds, somehow Graham had always seemed like an extension of her own soul. They'd both been unhappy, yet striving for a place in this wide world that felt right when they had found each other.

Why did that have to change now?

Caitlin bit her lip. Right words or not, she had to make him see things her way. "If I'm your wife, Gray, I have to live with you."

She didn't want to go to her own home. She wanted to start their life together. However awkward those first steps were going to be, they had to be taken. If they weren't, none of this would ever gain any more length and breadth than it had right at this moment.

The charade would never become reality.

"Besides." She forged on. "I want to meet your mother and your son."

They were stopped at a light. Graham paused, thinking, wrestling with his thoughts. He supposed she was making sense. When the light changed, he signaled, switching lanes beyond the intersection until he was on the extreme left. He made a U-turn at the next light, retracing his steps. Taking her to his home the way she requested.

Caitlin hung on as the car shifted, a big, lumbering buffalo in a sleek, feline world. She couldn't help grinning. "Doesn't exactly turn on a dime, does it?"

"She," he corrected, a hint of a smile glinting on his lips.

Her eyes opened wide as she stared at him. "Your car's a she?"

Graham nodded, easing through another yellow light. "Esmerelda."

"You named your car?" The laugh throbbed in her throat as she posed the question to him incredulously.

He spared her a look as he took another corner. "What's so funny?"

"Nothing." This time she did laugh, with pure delight. And a measure of relief. "Gray, there's hope for you yet."

He had no idea what she was talking about. Only that Caitlin had questioned his car's abilities. He had a soft spot in his heart for the vehicle. His eyes flickered over the dashboard, the dashboard he cleaned and polished regularly.

"She handles well if you treat her right."

Maybe someday she'd hear the same affection in his voice when he spoke about her. "That goes for women, too, you know."

The glimmer grew into a full smile over his sensual lips. "Point taken."

Some of the tension abated and she let out a sigh as she sank back in the seat. "When do we meet with the judge?"

We. It had such a strong, secure sound. If he could only…

No, he couldn't. He couldn't let himself enjoy the illusion it conjured up. Of a home and family. A marriage that was something other than a sham for his son's sake. He might start to believe in it. This was a favor she was doing for him, nothing more. And he would return the favor by giving her her freedom as soon as it was possible.

"Wednesday."

This was Saturday. Not much time for her to settle in to a routine. But it could be done. Caitlin nodded.

"Just tell me the time and I'll be ready." She smiled at him. "Don't worry. In case you've forgotten, you've just married the daughter of a very prominent family in the community. The Cassidys practically founded Arizona and have always been heavily involved in the social and political scene here." Her mind was racing, forming possibilities. Backup plans in case something went awry. "The judge is bound to take all that into consideration. Jake isn't going anywhere."

No, he thought, approaching the small community where he lived, he hadn't forgotten Caitlin's lineage. That was the problem. For a short time he had been able to place it aside. But he knew now that it would have popped up to haunt him.

There would be no way he could repay her for what she was doing for him, Graham thought. But he could try. That meant keeping his distance from her. He couldn't have his own needs clouding his judgment. And they seemed to cloud up every time he was near her.

Graham pulled up in front of his house. He turned off the engine, but made no move to get out. Instead, he turned toward her. He wanted to give her one last chance to change her mind and go back to her own house.

Leaning his arm along the back of the seat, he tried to filter out the way she had felt in his arms last night. Her scent seemed to be filling up all the spaces in his car, surrounding him.

"This isn't going to be easy."

"Nothing worthwhile ever is." *Oh, no,* Caitlin thought, *you're not talking me out of this.* "Just introduce me, Gray. I'll take it from there."

He laughed softly, sifting a lock of her hair through his fingers and watching it rain down on her shoulder. He wished things were different. That one of them was different.

But things were what they were and there was no changing them.

"Big words for someone so small."

She wanted to curl into his touch, but she remained on her own side of the car. Instead, she winked at him. "Hey, don't mess with me. I've got a big, strong husband to champion me now."

When she said that, her eyes sparkled, making his knees weak. But it wasn't a game. This was serious. And he wasn't her husband. Not really. "Cait—"

She placed her fingers to his lips and shook her head. She didn't want to hear any more disclaimers. "Just open the front door." With that, she slid out of the car.

Caitlin followed Graham up the short brick front walk. Despite her bravado, nerves began to drum through her. More than anything, she wanted his family to like her. And she wanted to like them. Caitlin had always been aware of her own lineage. She had a pedigree. But, aside from her father, she had never really felt as if she had a family.

She wanted this to be her family. In a way, she supposed she was as hungry as he for acceptance.

Graham glanced at Caitlin as she joined him at the door. She was almost pale, he thought. A moment before he placed the key into the lock he covered her hand with his own and squeezed it.

Caitlin looked at him in surprise. She opened her mouth to say something, but he was already unlocking the door.

Within a moment the lower half of his body was wrapped in as huge a hug as Jake could manage.

"Hey, what's this?" His own arms went around the boy's slight shoulders. Jake's greetings were usually enthusiastic, but nothing like this.

Jake remained with his face buried against his father's stomach. Even at this age, he was keenly aware that a man didn't show tears. Or fear. His grandmother had said so. He didn't want to dishonor his father by behaving like a baby.

But he had been afraid last night when his father hadn't come home again. Afraid that he had been abandoned a second time. "Dad, I thought you were never coming back."

Graham gently moved his son back, holding him by the shoulders. He studied the small, solemn face. "Hey, I said I'd be back."

Jake nodded. "Yeah, but things happen."

Things happen. That was the way he had explained Celia's abrupt departure to the boy. He hugged Jake to him. There was no way he was going to leave this boy, or have him taken from him. Graham glanced at Caitlin, unaware that there was gratitude in his eyes.

But she saw it and hugged it to her. Another tiny piece of the wall between them had come down, she thought.

"Those kinds of things *don't* happen," Graham assured his son fiercely.

That seemed to placate Jake. He looked up, suddenly aware that his father hadn't returned alone. Jake stared at Caitlin. "Who's this?"

Before Gray could answer, Caitlin dropped to one knee. She wanted to be on eye level with the boy, recalling how much she had always hated having adults look down at her as if she was somehow beneath them.

"Hi, Jake, my name's Caitlin." His eyes were soft and brown. Like hot chocolate, she thought. Like Graham's. "Your dad does nothing but talk about you."

The statement coaxed a broad smile from Jake's lips, but it was obvious that he was still reserving final judgment on her. He turned toward his father. "Why is she here, Dad?"

Caitlin rose and saw the discomfort in Graham's eyes.

Can't tell them, can you? Is it so hard for you say that I'm your wife, Gray? Even if it's just supposed to be make-believe?

She looked at Jake as Graham searched for the right words. "I'm here to make sure you stay with your dad for as long as you want."

Jake's mouth fell open. "Are you magic?"

Graham's eyes met Caitlin's over the boy's head. "Almost," Graham murmured.

The comment made her smile warmly.

Jake's eyes were huge. "Really?"

It wasn't fair to tease him like this. "No, but I am going to make sure that you stay here with your dad," Caitlin promised firmly.

It was a promise she intended to live up to no matter what it took. Especially now that she had seen the boy, seen the love that shone in his eyes when he looked up at his father. They belonged together. And she had the resources at her disposal to insure it. She knew that Graham wouldn't want her interfering like that, but, if it became necessary, she would. What he didn't know wouldn't hurt him.

Caitlin became aware of another figure in the room, a small, silent figure. The stately woman wore a long-sleeved red blouse and a light blue skirt whose hem seemed to whisper along the floor when she moved. Her blue-black hair was completely devoid of silver and she wore it in two thick, long braids bound in leather that hung midway down her back.

Graham's mother.

Summoning her courage, Caitlin smiled at her. The woman's eyes washed over her carefully, as if absorbing every detail. The smile wasn't returned.

Caitlin saw the resemblance instantly. The high cheekbones. The regal bearing. The solemn look. They were mother and son, all right.

Suddenly nervous again, Caitlin curled her fingers into her palms and glanced at Graham, waiting. The next step was his.

Releasing his son, he moved toward his mother and pressed a kiss to her temple. "Hello, Ma."

Lily Redhawk's eyes never left Caitlin even as she acknowledged Graham's greeting. "You have brought company."

He paused for a moment, knowing that this wasn't going to be received well. After her own experience, his mother was staunchly against marrying outside the tribe. "I've brought a little more than that, Ma."

Her soft eyes shifted toward her son's face. He didn't need to explain. She understood a great deal of what was in her son's heart without benefit of words.

Moving forward, Lily placed a hand on her grandson's shoulder. The boy shifted closer to her, closing ranks. "She's the woman you once loved, isn't she?"

Caitlin felt as if she were a vapor, hovering disembodied in the air as they talked about her. Lily's voice was even, neither welcoming nor judgmental. Caitlin still felt cold. Though Gray wasn't the type to vocalize what happened to him, his mother probably had some idea of what had transpired eleven years ago. She couldn't think well of her, Caitlin thought. Not without the facts that had come to light so recently.

Caitlin couldn't blame her. That still didn't make standing here like this any easier for her.

"There was some misunderstanding then," Caitlin began, hoping to explain. If she was going to convince Gray that this marriage was going to work, she needed this woman as her ally, not someone who would stand in judgment of her and find her lacking.

Lily didn't appear to be interested in anything that Caitlin might have to say in her defense. "Young people always misunderstand."

She looked at her son, waiting for him to explain the young woman's presence in her home. A home she shared with her grandson and him.

"Ma, Jake," Graham began, then stopped. He looked at his mother and then picked Jake up in his arms.

Caitlin stood apart, feeling as if a line had just been drawn in the sand. They were on one side and she on the other. An appendage. And a distant one, at that.

Sensing the discomfort she had to be going through, Graham moved closer to her. He took her hand in his, silently giving her his support. "Caitlin and I were married last night."

Silence met his announcement.

Maybe if she helped ease them all into this, Caitlin thought, it would be less difficult to adjust to. "It's just a temporary arrangement." She looked from the boy's small face to Lily's. "Graham needs to show the court that he can provide a good, two-parent home for Jake. And my family has some influence."

Not that her mother would exercise any in this case, Caitlin added silently. But if necessary, she knew she could prevail on her lawyer to pull some strings. Graham might not like it, but by marrying her, he had made this her fight as well as his. And she didn't like to lose. That much she had gotten from her mother.

Jake's face was a mirror of confusion. He looked from his father to the woman beside him. She had a nice smile and he liked her eyes. But his mother had a nice smile, too, and she had left. "Does that make you my mom?"

She tried to read in his eyes whether or not the idea pleased him. She had no more success than she had with his father. "If you'd like me to be. I know that I'd like that very much."

He pressed his lips together, undecided. "I'll think about it."

Yes, she thought, he was Graham's son.

"Ben called," Lily said abruptly. "He said you were to go down to the station as soon as you arrived. Something about an arraignment."

He'd completely forgotten. He was due in court at three. Damn.

Graham placed Jake on the floor. "Thanks." He nodded at his mother.

He was leaving, she thought, a surge of panic washing over her before she could stop it. "I thought you called in for a personal day."

He hated to leave her like this, but maybe it was for the best. Maybe she could settle in better without him. "I did, but I forgot that Ben and I have to testify at an arraignment this afternoon." And he was going to be late if he didn't hurry. "I'll see you all later tonight."

He paused at the door, looking at Caitlin. She'd sounded almost eager when she had referred to this as a temporary arrangement just now. He was right. She really didn't want to be tied to this any more than he wanted to tie her to it. It was a favor, nothing more. He had to keep reminding himself of that.

"Good luck," he mouthed.

She nodded. Big help he was.

The door closed and Caitlin stood, feeling nervous and deserted.

You asked for this, she told herself.

She turned toward the others. Jake was looking up at her. But when she reached out to him, he suddenly ran off to his room without a word and closed the door. The slam echoed through the house.

That left her and Graham's mother. She looked toward the woman, hoping some sort of a bridge could be formed or at least begun. Instead, the woman silently turned on her heel and walked out of the room.

"And then there was one," Caitlin murmured to herself.

Well, this was going great so far. She felt as welcome as Custer riding into Little Big Horn. Or as welcome as Graham had been on his first day at school, she recalled. With his dark good looks and his noble, defensive carriage, he had stood out in the crowd. And stood apart.

If he could survive that, she could put up with this.

She looked around the living room. Traces of his heritage, of his roots, were everywhere. She found it somehow touching that a handwoven blanket hung on the wall with a Colorado Rockies pennant beside it.

Time, that's all. She was just going to need time to win them all over.

That, she mused, was giving herself a hell of a lot of credit.

She needed a friendly voice to talk to. She thought of Kerry and went off in search of a telephone. Wandering through the house, Caitlin found a wall phone in the kitchen. She tapped out the number of the shop, glancing around.

There was a room off to the side. Another bedroom, she guessed as the telephone on the other end rang. Probably his mother's.

"Naughty But Nice, how may I help you?"

"Kerry?" God, but it felt good to hear her friend's voice. Caitlin wound the cord around her fingers. There was nowhere to sit, so she stood.

"Caitlin." Kerry's voice immediately became animated. "Where *are* you?"

No-man's-land. Strike that. No-woman's-land. "At Graham's house."

"Oh, thank God." The worried tone left her voice. It was replaced by a warm, envious note. "Another hot night, eh?"

"You might say that." Caitlin thought of framing this properly, then just blurted the fact out. "I married Graham last night, Kerry."

There was half a second's pause. "Wow. Talk about a fast worker. When you decide to get moving, you don't waste time."

Caitlin knew how Kerry's mind worked. She probably thought of all this as hopelessly romantic. If only it was. "It's not exactly like that. His ex-wife is trying to gain custody of his son. Gray needs a wife to round out the scene. I volunteered.''

Kerry laughed in disbelief. ''You mean there was a job opening like that and I missed it? Boy, some women have all the luck.'' And then she stopped teasing. She'd seen the look on both their faces in unguarded moments. If she was any judge, this was a union that was meant to be. ''Make the most of it, Cait. I know if it were me, I wouldn't let him go.''

Caitlin looked down at her hand and the wedding band. She moved it absently with her thumb. It wasn't that simple. If, at the end of this, Gray still wanted his freedom, she wouldn't withhold it.

''I love him, Kerry,'' she whispered.

''Then what I just said goes doubly.'' Kerry heard things in Caitlin's voice that her friend wasn't saying. ''What's the matter?''

''He brought me home to meet his mother and son, then had to leave for the precinct.'' She knew it was childish, but she felt abandoned. ''They both went into their rooms as soon as the door was closed.'' She stared at the door off the kitchen. ''I'm standing alone here, feeling like Daniel in the lion's den.''

Kerry felt for her. ''Then make friends with the lions. Daniel did.''

''Yeah, maybe.'' Easier said than done. Kerry hadn't seen the uncertain look in Jake's eyes. Or the distant, hostile one in Lily's.

''It's either that or get eaten alive.'' Kerry knew Caitlin hated pep talks, so she kept it short. ''Look, if you can face up to your mother, you can face up to anything—no offense.''

''None taken.'' She laughed. Kerry always made her feel better about things. And she was right. Lily Redhawk had nothing on Regina Cassidy when it came to slicing someone off at the knees. She'd dueled with an expert and lived to tell about it. ''Kerry, I won't be in today.''

''I kind of figured that out on my own.'' Kerry's voice softened. ''Keep me posted, okay?''

Caitlin smiled. "Okay," she promised.

She hung up and looked toward the bedroom. The door was still closed. Caitlin squared her shoulders and thought of Kerry's comment about Daniel and the lions.

Here goes nothing, she thought.

Or everything.

Chapter 14

For a moment Caitlin stood before Lily's bedroom door, gathering her courage to her. It would have been much easier just to walk away, to let some time lapse before she spoke with Graham's mother. Maybe let her adjust to the idea.

Caitlin frowned, annoyed with herself. She was rationalizing. If she waited, the situation would only get worse, not better. And her own anxiety would only build, not lessen.

But it wasn't easy looking into a person's eyes and seeing only dislike reflected there.

This is what you went through, isn't it, Gray?

She knew it was. It was what Gray had felt when he had faced her mother, when he had faced the people she had once thought of as friends. Relating, understanding, Caitlin was more determined than ever to make up for anything he had endured for her sake.

That would mean convincing the thickheaded jerk that they belonged together, no matter what he might believe to the contrary. And that meant getting his mother's blessing.

Or at the very least, negating Lily Redhawk's tacit disapproval.

Her head was beginning to hurt.

Caitlin knocked softly on the door. Her heart amplified the sound within her chest. When there was no answer, she raised her hand to knock again.

"Come in." The command was quiet, but there was no mistaking the authority behind it.

Drawing a deep breath, Caitlin turned the knob and walked in.

The room Lily Redhawk occupied was small and Spartan-like, save for the colorful, handwoven blanket on her bed and a loom against the wall. Her back was to the door and her activity was centered around the creased leather valise lying openmouthed on her bed. She was packing.

Caitlin wet her lips. They felt incredibly dry, like her throat. "Mrs. Redhawk—"

Lily looked at her sharply. A dress hovered in mid-descent into the suitcase. "I was Mrs. Warren," she corrected without emotion. "Redhawk is my father's name. And mine."

So what did she call her? Mom? Somehow Caitlin doubted it. At a loss, she let the salutation go and nodded toward the suitcase. She felt as if the ground beneath her feet were liquefying.

"Are you going somewhere?"

Lily placed the dress on top of the small pile of clothing within the case. "Back to the reservation. To my hogan."

Though Lily's movements were unhurried, Caitlin had the feeling that this was a decision born in the past few minutes. And it had to do with her.

She sought the right words from amid a bramble of wrong ones. "For a visit?"

Lily had turned away and didn't bother to look at her now. "To live."

Oh, terrific. Not here ten minutes and already she was chasing his mother away. This was going to go over great with Gray. She had to find a way to stop her.

"Because of me?"

Lily paused for half a heartbeat, then continued packing. "You are the wife here now. A mother is not needed."

At a complete loss, Caitlin dragged her hand through her hair. She hadn't expected to be welcomed with open arms, but she hadn't expected to instigate an exodus, either. She didn't think Gray was going to be happy about this turn of events. Caitlin knew she wasn't. She wasn't trying to force anyone from their home, she was attempting to preserve it.

Helpless, desperate, she had only instincts to guide her. Maybe that was enough. She certainly hoped so.

Caitlin moved around the bed so that Lily was forced to look at her. "A mother is always needed."

The woman raised her eyes to Caitlin's face, pausing for a long time. Caitlin felt she was being examined fiber by fiber.

She pressed on, not knowing if she was on sure footing or quicksand. "Gray would be very upset if he came home to find that you'd gone. And Jake still needs you. I intend to go on working. If Gray has his way, nothing is going to change around here." Her eyes met the woman's. Her own were imploring. "That's why I'm here. To make sure nothing changes."

Lily stopped packing. Her eyes were like tiny twin beams of light to Caitlin, boring into her soul. "Is that the only reason?"

Caitlin shrugged evasively. "The only reason that Gray sees."

There was no smile on her face, but something softened in Lily's eyes. "But you do not."

Caitlin thought of denying it, but there didn't seem to be much point. She was never comfortable with lies and she had a feeling this regal-looking woman could see through them, anyway.

"No. I don't. I like your son, Mrs.—" Oh, what was the use? "I love him," Caitlin amended helplessly. "I always have."

If she was swayed by Caitlin's words, there was no indication. "But you ran from him."

So she knew. Caitlin wondered how much of the story his mother was aware of. Probably just enough to condemn her.

"I thought he ran from me." She wasn't being defensive,

she just wanted his mother to know how it had been. Caitlin had a feeling that pleading would leave Lily Redhawk unaffected. "It was a huge misunderstanding that neither one of us was smart enough to unravel at the time."

Lily nodded, understanding. Remembering how it had once been for her. Her father's warning ringing in ears that refused to hear. "Because your emotions clouded the way."

"Yes." Eager to capitalize on the headway, Caitlin sat on the bed, talking to this woman she hardly knew in a way she never could to her own mother. "The point is, we're married now and I'm going to need your help."

Lily showed no surprise, merely suspicion. Maybe she had a right, Caitlin thought. "Why?"

Caitlin spread her hands helplessly. She wasn't even sure just what it was she needed help with. Maybe everything. "To show me the way."

Lily's eyes never wavered from hers. "Back to Graham's heart?"

The question surprised her. That was it, in a nutshell. "Yes."

Then she didn't know, Lily thought. "You are already there."

Caitlin shook her head. There his mother was wrong. Very wrong. She might have been there once, but she wasn't there now. Gray wouldn't let her in.

She stared down at the blanket on the bed, a beautiful design of blues, reds and blacks. Caitlin ran her hand over it slowly, absorbing the texture, the workmanship. Touching part of what Gray was.

"No, he's made that perfectly clear. He thinks what happened between us was for the best."

Lily thought of her own marriage. Of the sadness that had engulfed the happiness, swallowing it whole until it was as if it had never existed at all. "Perhaps he is right."

When Caitlin looked up at Lily, her eyes were sure, determined. Almost fierce. Lily was impressed.

"No, he's not. I'm sure of it. I just have to find a way to convince him that I'm not happier on that damn pedestal he keeps trying to put me on." She rose, her thoughts making her restless. "That he thinks I belong on." Caitlin took the woman's hands in hers. The urgency she felt was silently telegraphed to Lily. "And I won't be able to if he thinks that his own mother doesn't want to remain in the same house with me. If he thinks that I chased her away."

"No one chases me away." For a moment Lily allowed her hands to remain in Caitlin's. She studied the young face before her. Silently she withdrew her hands. And then, turning, Lily removed the ceremonial dress she had just placed in the suitcase.

Relieved, Caitlin once again covered the small, delicate hands with her own. "Thank you."

The woman nodded, a princess granting a petitioner a boon. Caitlin edged toward the door. "I'll just leave you to unpack."

There was no acknowledgment of her words, so Caitlin slipped out of the room.

"You may call me Lily."

The words, addressed to her back, trailed after Caitlin. She turned, smiling. Her gratitude and relief were in her eyes.

"Lily," Caitlin repeated, savoring the favor that was implied. "It's a beautiful name."

The woman vaguely lifted her shoulders and then let them fall as she worked. "It is just a name."

Caitlin left her to her unpacking. Hope was pushing open the door that Graham had attempted to shut on her. One down, one to go.

Jake's room faced the front of the house. Caitlin approached it with the same unsettled feeling she'd experienced approaching Lily's. Just because he was younger didn't mean that this was going to be any easier.

She smiled to herself just before she knocked. She felt like Jacob, toiling for seven years in the desert for Rachel. Caitlin wondered how Gray would like being thought of as Rachel.

Caitlin knocked on Jake's door and then slowly turned the doorknob, easing the door open. He was sitting cross-legged on the floor, playing with carved figures that were resplendent in ceremonial garb. One of them looked to be half-man, half-eagle.

She ventured a smile. "Hi."

"Hi," he echoed. He looked up at her, waiting to see what she wanted.

Caitlin dropped to the floor beside him. With a little effort she managed to imitate the position he had taken. "I just wanted to look in on you, Jake, to see what you were doing."

"Playing," he replied solemnly. There was just a touch of disgust in his voice. Anyone could see what he was doing.

He ignored her and continued playing. But after a minute he stopped. It was no use. The magic was gone from his figures. He laid them down and slanted a glance at her.

"Are you really going to be my mother?"

"Yes, if you want me to." She repeated her earlier qualification. Did he? It was not unlike walking on a tightrope wearing combat boots. She had absolutely no feeling if she was still on the wire or off it, about to plummet to the ground.

She peered at his face. "Do you?"

The thin shoulders jerked up and then down. "I don't know."

Yes, he did, she realized. He was a child hungry for a mother's love. But something was stopping him. "Why?"

There was pain etched into the innocent look in his eyes. "Because if you're my mother, I might like you."

She picked up one of the figures and pretended to examine it. It was a fierce-looking warrior, the upper part of his body encased in a pair of eagle's wings. "And that's a bad thing?"

"Yeah." He took the figure from her. The way, she wondered, that he wanted to take his father from her? "'Cause then you'll go, just like she did. Celia," he explained. "My mom left me." His lower lip protruded in a slight pout that he was trying to control.

"Oh, honey, I won't—"

Something within her hesitated. *Don't make promises you can't keep.*

He looked so upset. Could she promise him she wouldn't leave him when Graham had made it clear that she would?

But Jake was far too young to understand complex agreements between adults who had allowed their lives to get so tangled. He understood only loneliness.

As did she.

Her heart reached out to his. "I won't leave if you don't want me to."

Doubt still clouded his face, but he looked as if he wanted to believe her. Badly. "Promise?"

"Promise." Caitlin nodded, unable to say anything further because of the lump in her throat. She took a breath, steadying herself. "So it's okay if you want to like me." She reached out and touched his dark, silky hair, curving her hand along his face fondly. "I promise I'll never hurt you."

He looked at her just the way his grandmother had. Just the way his father did. As if he could see something that was just beneath the surface. Something most people couldn't see.

"Okay. I'll think about it." But the sunny smile that rose to his lips told Caitlin he already had. And made his decision, as well.

She held up the figure she'd picked up from the floor. "What's this one called?"

"That's Talking God." Encouraged by her interest, he picked up the other figure and held it up for her inspection. "And this one's Corn Woman." It was something he had grown up with and he was surprised that everyone didn't know this. Jake cocked his head, his dark eyes bright, curious. "Don't you have them?"

She shook her head. "No, all I had were Barbie and Ken." She grinned at him as she handed the figure back to Jake. "I like these, though."

Jake stared down at the figure in his hand, debating. He thrust the one he'd referred to as Corn Woman toward her. "You can keep this one, if you like. While you're here," he qualified.

She wondered if he understood that he was attempting to bribe her. Probably. He might be young but he was shrewd. Like his father.

She smiled at him, touched by the offer and what it represented. "Thank you." Caitlin looked down at the figure in her hand. "I'm afraid I'll hurt it, though." She offered Corn Woman back to him. "Would you keep it safe for me?"

He accepted the figure with all the solemnity of a soldier charged with guarding a dignitary. If Gray had married her all those years ago, they might have had a son like this now. She felt cheated and sentimental all at the same time.

"Would you mind very much if I hugged you?" she asked softly.

Jake looked at her, obviously surprised by the question. "Why?"

Not your typical child, she thought. But then, being Gray's, she wouldn't have expected him to be. "Because I'd very much like to."

He seemed to be thinking it over, then shrugged. "Okay." He set down the wooden figures so that neither they nor she would be hurt.

Caitlin encircled his slight shoulders and drew him into her arms. It felt wonderful to hold the child, to hold a part of Graham that he deemed precious. He felt like heaven in her arms.

Very slowly she released him. They smiled at each other, both shy over the feelings that had passed between them.

"You smell good."

She laughed, rising to her feet. "Thank you."

A soft, chanting sound wafted through the window. It seemed to be coming from the yard just behind Jake's room. The song didn't sound like anything she'd ever heard before.

Caitlin looked at the boy, puzzled. "What's that?"

"Grandma." Seeing that Caitlin didn't quite comprehend, Jake scrambled to his feet and took her hand. "C'mon, I'll show you."

He took Caitlin through the house to the back door, which led into their yard. A high wooden fence, long since bleached by the sun, ran along the perimeter, keeping out uninvited eyes. Caitlin felt a little like an intruder.

Lily Redhawk was in the backyard, wearing the dress that Caitlin had seen her packing earlier. She was chanting words

Caitlin didn't understand. They melded with the air and became one with the land.

As Caitlin watched, the woman carefully sprinkled colored mineral powders down on what looked to be a layer of sand. Beneath the colorful spray, figures were forming in the sand.

Caitlin bent and whispered into Jake's ear. "What is she doing?"

"Sand painting," he told her matter-of-factly. He shook his head at Caitlin's ignorance. He forgave her because she was pretty. "She's singing a Blessingway song. Grandma's a medicine woman," he told Caitlin proudly, his voice low. "Like her father was."

Caitlin watched, fascinated, as Lily continued to chant and draw, the colorful powders raining from her nimble fingers. If Lily was aware of their presence, she made no sign until she was finished.

Something within the chanting sound spoke to Caitlin and comforted her. She had no idea how long she stood there, observing.

Finally it was done. Lily lightly dusted her hands one against the other and stepped away from the sand painting. Only then did she turn and raise her eyes to Caitlin's.

Was she supposed to be here? Would the woman become angry because she had watched? Caitlin had a feeling that she wouldn't be. That she was meant to see this.

"It's lovely," Caitlin told her.

Lily accepted her due. "It is to ask the Holy People to bless your marriage and this house." Having said that, she turned and walked into the house.

A sand painting. To bless her marriage to Graham. Caitlin drew closer to inspect it as Jake lingered patiently on the side. It seemed incredibly beautiful to her.

Sunshine burst through her veins as she looked at the boy. "Does this mean your grandmother likes me?"

He shrugged. "I think so. With Grandma, sometimes it's hard to tell."

With your father, too, she thought as she took Jake's hand in hers and followed Lily into the house.

* * *

It had been a long day, especially since he'd had next to no sleep. Graham had purposely lingered at the precinct, attempting to catch up on his paperwork. If it hadn't been there, he would have found another excuse not to go home.

He still hadn't had enough time to come to terms with what he'd done. With the turn his life had taken. He knew he should be happy. Caitlin was right. This was the solution he needed, the weapon that would enable him to fight for what was his. And win.

But he wasn't happy. He wasn't happy at all. He felt as if he were being tested.

And that he would be found lacking.

God, if it had been anyone but Caitlin…

But it was Caitlin and he was going to have to make his peace with that.

When Graham finally returned home, it was past ten-thirty. Caitlin's car was parked in the driveway. Obviously she'd gotten someone to give her a ride to her house. Kerry, probably.

Shutting off the engine, Graham sat in the driveway, wishing he was somewhere else. Or that Caitlin was.

He passed his hand over his face, then blew out a long breath. It was late. Maybe she was asleep. If she was, he'd just stretch out on the sofa.

He'd planned to, anyway. It would keep things simpler. And keep him away from temptation.

Some warrior he would have made. Afraid of a woman. He got out of the car, slamming the door behind him. No, it wasn't the woman he was afraid of. It was himself, and what was inside—a need for her that was so huge, so overwhelming, it frightened him.

Graham let himself in and walked through the house to the kitchen. He was hot and tired. The temperature outside was a cool ninety-nine degrees and he was almost well-done. It was a mystery to him how his ancestors could have lived out their days on the desert without migrating somewhere else.

Reaching into the refrigerator, Graham took out a half-filled pitcher of lemonade and poured himself a tall glass. Drinking, he turned and saw the light seeping out from beneath his mother's door.

She was still awake.

He thought of going to her, then changed his mind. Whatever he had to say could wait until morning. Maybe it would make more sense by then.

The next moment his mother's door opened. She walked into the kitchen and he knew that she had been waiting for him. "You are late."

He shrugged as he drained the rest of his drink. "It couldn't be helped. I had some things to take care of at the precinct."

It was an excuse. Her son was running from something. She'd never known him to do that before. "You have some 'things' to take care of here, as well."

"Yeah, I know." He set his glass in the sink, carefully choosing his words. There weren't any to appropriately cover this situation. Especially considering the way she felt about marrying out of the tribe.

"Look, Ma, I know I kind of dropped this on you without warning, but—"

Lily cut his explanation short. "She asked me to stay."

His dark brows gathered together. Had she somehow gotten the wrong idea? "I don't want you to leave—"

Some things were understood. "No, but when a man takes a wife—"

He threw up his hands in a rare show of impatience toward her. "I already told you, this is just an arrangement between us to keep Celia from taking Jake away."

Lily wondered if he truly believed what he was saying. If he had managed to fool himself. "I think she hopes for more than that."

He shrugged, looking out into the yard. He thought he saw something on the ground. A sand painting? It was probably just the way the moon was hitting the ground. He turned back to look at his mother.

"She understands," he said firmly.

"Does she?" Lily raised her eyes to his, challenging his words. "Do you?"

He was far too tired to get into a philosophical debate. "Ma, it's late."

"Yes." She nodded her agreement. "And you belong with your new wife," she said pointedly as she stepped into the hall. "Jake likes her."

Well, that hadn't taken long. "And you?" Graham couldn't help asking. "Do you like her?" It wouldn't change anything, but he was curious.

She didn't answer his question, but she gave him an answer of sorts. "I like peace and harmony."

Lily stood in her doorway, waiting for him to leave the shelter of the kitchen. He had no choice. Walking down the hall, he opened his bedroom door and crossed the threshold.

Caitlin was there, lying asleep in his bed. A thin sheet covered her body, clinging to the outline. It was highlighted by silvery strands that descended from the moon, caressing her like long gossamer fingers.

Desires tugged at him, fierce in their demands. Calling for tribute. It would have taken him so little to give in.

Just one more time.

But one more time would feed into another and another, pushing him into an emotional quagmire that he wouldn't be able to pull himself free of.

He hesitated just inside the doorway, struggling against a temptation so fierce it took his breath away. Behind him he heard his mother's door close. It made his decision for him.

Graham withdrew from the room.

Caitlin watched him through slitted eyes, waiting. Hoping. But then the door closed again and she was alone.

As she had been all night.

Chapter 15

The Highland Street courthouse was a shining example of modern architecture. All tinted glass and girders, it maximized the benefits of the perpetual Phoenix sun by taking out its sting and filtering what remained into the building. The offices were awash in light.

The corridors, however, were boxed in by walls and closed doors, gaining their illumination from fluorescent lighting discreetly hidden overhead. Somehow, that added to the foreboding atmosphere reserved for places where justice was purportedly meted out.

At the behest of his family, Caitlin's father had become a lawyer. She wasn't unfamiliar with places like this. He'd brought her to the courthouse with him more than once when meeting a friend or when last-minute details necessitated his presence. He wanted his daughter to see where he pleaded his cases.

She'd been in awe then. But that was because her father had made everything seem wonderful. She tried to imagine how this place would look to a seven-year-old seeing it for the first time. A seven-year-old who didn't have a father to make this into a grand adventure for him.

As if sensing her thoughts, Jake tugged on his father's arm. "When this is over, Dad, am I gonna go home with you and Caitlin?" A sliver of fear echoed in the uncertain voice.

As he walked down the corridor bracketed by Caitlin and Graham, Jake had his hand tucked into his father's as if that would keep him safe.

She knew the feeling. There was something about Gray's presence that made you feel no harm would ever penetrate the aura he cast.

But he wasn't answering his son. Glancing at Graham, Caitlin saw the debate warring in his eyes. He was torn between comforting Jake and preparing him for what might happen. This wasn't a time to be completely honest.

"Yes," she answered firmly. "You're coming home with us."

Graham looked at her over his son's head. Now that they were just minutes away from the informal hearing in the judge's chambers, he didn't want to make promises to the boy that might be overturned by a whimsical magistrate. Ultimately, Jake would remain his, one way or another. Even if he had to move heaven and earth to accomplish it.

But as far as the immediate situation went, fate might have different ideas.

He didn't want to undermine Jake's confidence in him by promising him one thing and then having the exact opposite happen.

Hedging, he tried to brace Jake for the worst. "You might have to visit with your mother for a little while, but then—"

"No." Jake pulled his hand free and dug his brand-new shoes into the patterned vinyl floor, refusing to move. "I don't want to." His eyes were huge, frightened. He didn't remember his mother very well. All he remembered was that she'd left him. And his father hadn't. "I want to stay with you."

Jake was begging. She couldn't stand it. Caitlin took his hand and squeezed, silently comforting him. "Then you will."

He looked from his father to Caitlin, hope shining in his dark brown eyes. "No matter what?"

"No matter what." It would have been cruel to say anything else.

It wasn't her place to guarantee that, Graham thought angrily. She had no right. "Cait—"

She heard the sharp edge in Graham's voice and ignored it. It wasn't difficult. For the past few days they'd been almost like strangers. He'd found one reason after another not to come to her bed at night. And she had fallen asleep without him. It was as if those two nights they had enjoyed in each other's arms had never happened and he was determined to stick to his word, making this a marriage of convenience.

His convenience, perhaps, but not hers.

She smiled at Jake, winding her fingers around his. "We're going to be late, Gray."

Caitlin began walking down the corridor again. Graham followed, his silent censure enshrouding her.

At the end of the hall she saw a tall, rangy-looking man wearing a conservative beige suit and holding a worn briefcase, which he kept shifting from hand to hand. He was obviously waiting for someone.

She glanced at Graham for confirmation. He nodded. The man was their lawyer. Caitlin had resisted the temptation of calling her own lawyer, choosing for the moment to go with the one that Graham had retained. He wanted it that way. She hoped they wouldn't regret it.

The man snapped to attention when he saw them approach. Shifting his briefcase to his left hand, he extended his right one to Graham.

"I was beginning to get worried." Shaking his client's hand, the man looked at Caitlin. Mild interest flickered in his eyes. "And you're Mrs. Redhawk?"

"Caitlin," she amended, shaking his hand.

"Zach Neubert." His grip was warm, firm. The smile on his face was relieved and genuine. Caitlin began to feel better about the case. "You don't know how glad I am that you decided to move up your wedding date."

Opening the judge's outer door, he ushered them all in before the secretary. "This puts an entire new spin on the case. It gives us a fighting chance."

As he closed the door behind him, Zach nodded at the judge's secretary. The woman left the room to inform the judge that they had arrived.

Jake had gotten lost in the shuffle of bodies, and pushed his way forward. He looked up at his father, interpreting the strange man's words the only way he knew how.

"Fighting? Are you and Mom going to fight?" If he tried hard, Jake could remember angry words and doors being slammed around him. He wasn't sure who had done the slamming, only that he remembered feeling afraid. He didn't want to feel that way again.

"It's just a phrase, honey," Caitlin assured the boy quickly, exchanging glances with the lawyer.

Zach gave Caitlin a flustered look. He wasn't accustomed to talking around children or screening his words. He addressed himself to Graham.

"We've drawn Judge Harrison," he began again. "He's a traditionalist, so we may have our work cut out for us. There's always appeal, of course. I can have the case tied up for—"

Caitlin hadn't paid attention to the nameplate when they'd walked into the room. She made a point of looking at it now.

"William Henry Harrison," she read aloud. *Small world.*

"Yes." Zach looked at her. "Do you know him?" he asked guardedly. Depending on what capacity Graham's wife knew the judge in, the news could be either good or bad.

Unless something terrible happened in the judge's chambers, they were home free. Caitlin breathed a sigh of relief as she grinned at Graham. He raised a quizzical brow, waiting for an explanation.

"Yes, I know him." She ruffled Jake's hair. Everything was going to be fine. "He and my father went to law school together. They initially clerked at the same firm."

Zach reserved his enthusiasm. "And did they get along?"

Her grin grew larger. "My father got along with everyone." *Even my mother,* she added silently.

"Wonderful!" Zach clapped both hands over Caitlin's. "See if you can nudge his memory a little," he urged. "Maybe mention your father…"

That wasn't going to be necessary. "I won't have to. The judge has a photographic memory."

"Yes, I know." He said it in the voice of someone who'd had firsthand experience with the judge's powers of recall. She gathered by Zach's expression that he didn't much care for the judge. For once she was grateful for her family connections.

Caitlin looked at Graham and wondered why he looked so solemn. But then, he'd never been one to count on things going well.

The secretary returned and left the door behind her standing open. "The judge will see you now." She gestured toward Harrison's chambers. Zach led the way in.

As Jake followed next to his father, the judge's secretary placed a gentle hand on his shoulder, restraining him. "I'm afraid you're going to have to stay out here with me for a while."

Jake pulled away from her and hid behind his father. "Dad?"

It broke his heart to see Jake like this, afraid, the object of a tug-of-war every time he turned around. Graham gave his son a reassuring look and made no move to return him to the secretary.

"I thought the judge wanted to see all of us—as a family," Graham emphasized. The secretary looked at a loss for a reply. "It's the boy's future. Shouldn't he be included in the discussion?"

Without waiting for an answer, Graham took Jake's hand and ushered him into the judge's chambers. Caitlin was left alone to follow.

She felt like an appendage, but then, she had known when she'd gotten into this that it wasn't going to be easy. She'd deal with hurt feelings later. Right now, there was a judge to convince.

Judge William Henry Harrison was sitting at his desk when

they walked in, completely oblivious to their entrance. He had the ability to shut out everything except what he was concentrating on. At the moment he was reviewing the notes on the Redhawk custody case that had been compiled by his clerk.

The judge was a sober-looking man whose mouth turned down naturally. If it hadn't, the nature of his work would have made it so. He believed in man's inherent goodness and in the ability of the world to easily corrupt that goodness. He'd been married twice and widowed twice. His only daughter had run off at an early age and he had lost track of her by mutual consent. Over the years, optimism had receded from him and it was not his long suit.

To look at him now, it was difficult for Caitlin to reconcile her father's stories of their first-year escapades as fledgling lawyers. According to her father, Harrison's nickname had been Wild Willie and he had more than lived up to it.

Maybe he had devoted his life to living it down, she mused.

They took their seats. Jake reached for her hand and clutched it. Caitlin gave him a reassuring look. "It's going to be fine," she whispered in his ear. "You'll see."

The judge kept them waiting as he made a couple of last-minute notes. The computer that his secretary had insisted on sat dormant and vacant on the side of his desk. Harrison wrote everything longhand and left computers to the younger generation.

Finally laying down his pen, he peered over the top of his glasses at Zach. "And where is the other couple?"

"Right here, Your Honor," a deep baritone voice called out.

Caitlin turned and saw two men and a woman entering through the door they had just used. Both men looked as if they had stepped out of the same high-priced showroom, impeccably dressed in suits that bore exclusive labels. The taller of the two, a thin, dark-haired man, was escorting the woman.

So this was Celia.

Caitlin couldn't help glancing at Graham, looking for a tell-tale sign of emotion. He hadn't told her that Celia was beautiful. A distant part of her felt relieved when Graham's expression didn't soften. If anything, it hardened.

Their lawyer preceded them, perfunctorily shaking hands with Zach and offering a flurry of apologies to the judge. "The traffic was unusually heavy." The judge didn't seem interested. Excuses either bored or irritated him.

Caitlin saw only Celia. The woman was petite and she seemed born to the expensive tailored suit she wore. Her thick black hair was bound and twisted into a chignon. Unable to block it, Caitlin felt the unmistakable prick of jealousy. She could see why Graham had turned to Celia when he thought that she had rejected him.

Celia's dark eyes flickered over Caitlin, dismissing her as if she were just part of the furniture. They lingered longer on Graham, but it was the boy who was the object of her interest.

"Jake," she cried in surprise. It was obvious that she hadn't expected him to be here. She opened her arms to him eagerly.

Jake hesitated, then sank deeper against his father's side.

Harrison looked at Zach sharply, displeasure thinning his lips. "Mr. Neubert, what is this boy doing in my chambers?" He pointed toward his door. "Have him remain with my secretary until these proceedings are completed."

Panic entered Jake's eyes as Zach reached for his hand. "It's his fate being decided," Caitlin said quickly. "His father thought he should be present."

Judge Harrison's frown deepened as he looked at her, his eyes narrowing beneath iron-gray tufted brows. "Young woman—"

He paused suddenly, his mind rummaging through a thousand faces, searching for a match. He found one. The last time he had seen her was at her father's funeral. She'd worn sky blue, her father's favorite color.

"Caitlin?"

She smiled broadly. She'd wondered how long it would take him to remember. "Hello, Judge, how are you?"

This was the last place he'd have expected to run into her. Harrison leaned back in his chair, taking stock. He'd seen no mention of her in the case. Was she a friend of the boy's father?

"What are you doing here?"

Very deliberately Caitlin took Graham's hand in hers. Rather than closing ranks, she felt a distance and couldn't begin to understand why now, of all times. She blocked it as she concentrated on the judge. "I'm married to Detective Redhawk. Jake is my stepson."

"Married?" Harrison's eyes briefly shifted to Graham before looking at Caitlin again. "And your mother didn't invite me to the wedding?"

Because he had once been an old family friend, the judge would understand. "My mother wasn't invited to the wedding."

Her mother hadn't bothered to return her phone call, so Caitlin had refrained from any further attempts to get in contact with her. The idea of upbraiding Regina Cassidy for what she had done no longer mattered to Caitlin. It wasn't even a side bonus.

The judge nodded, just a hint of a smile flirting with the corners of his mouth. "I see." And he did. Regina Cassidy was a handsome woman by any standards. She was also a woman he would never have chosen as his own wife. It was a tribute to his late friend's easygoing nature that he had managed to survive all those years with her and still retain his sense of humor. Harrison knew that he wouldn't have been able to.

The judge cleared his throat. "Well, let's get on with this, shall we? I have a full docket today."

He paused for a moment as he looked carefully over the array of faces before him. Earlier, he'd been in some mental quandary about the case and its resolution. With this latest bit of information before him, the quandary no longer existed.

Folding his hands on the desk, he began by addressing both sides. "All things considered, you seem to be equally matched."

Albert Wells took immediate exception. "Your Honor, my client's husband is a highly respected businessman with a very secure financial portfolio. It's all there.'' He pointed to the manila folder on the judge's desk. He'd personally given the information to the judge's clerk. ''I am sure that you will agree that he and the child's mother are in a position to give the boy a great many advantages that he might not know if he remains with his adoptive father.''

There was no mistaking the belittling look he gave Graham. Caitlin felt her temper rising and she looked at Zach to take exception. Wells couldn't be allowed to get away with insulting Gray like that.

But as Zach opened his mouth, the judge waved him into silence. ''I noticed, Mr. Wells, that you mentioned the word *adoptive* in reference to Detective Redhawk, but not in reference to the boy's mother.'' Harrison's expression grew stern. Caitlin could well imagine the man posing for a sculpture of a gargoyle. ''They are both adoptive parents, Mr. Wells, and I'd like you to remember that. It is that fact that makes their initial claim so balanced.''

Wells shifted within his five-hundred-dollar jacket. ''I am aware of that, Your Honor—''

''Good.'' The judge nodded. But as Wells began to say something further, the judge neatly cut into his words. He had taken a personal dislike to the man and his attitude. And it showed. ''Are you also aware of Detective Redhawk's wife's standing in the community?''

Wells frowned as he looked accusingly at his counterpart. Zach met his glare head-on without flinching. ''No. I wasn't even aware that he had a wife, Your Honor, until last Friday.'' He leaned over the desk to gain Harrison's ear, or so he hoped. ''This is obviously just a ploy—''

If any sort of defamation of character was his goal, Wells was never allowed to reach it.

Harrison's eyes narrowed behind his glasses. ''I know the detective's wife, Mr. Wells. I bounced her on my knee. As I recall, she wet it.'' The judge didn't smile. Caitlin and Jake were the only ones in the room who did. ''Unless her character has undergone a drastic change, she is not in the habit of 'ploys.'

"But," he continued, "in the interest of justice and fairness, I will ask." Turning his attention to Caitlin, the judge leaned back in his black padded chair and studied her face solemnly. He was not above putting people on the spot. Not to see them twist and squirm, but to get at the unvarnished truth. Elbow on the desk, he leaned forward. "Why did you marry this man, Caitlin? *Was* it just to even things out for him?"

"No, Your Honor." She glanced at Graham before she continued. He didn't like sharing incidents in his life. But there was no other way. "Gray and I were going to be married eleven years ago."

The judge appeared unmoved by the information as he digested it. "What happened?"

"Mother." Caitlin saw that there was very little need to continue. "Wild Willie" knew exactly the kind of woman her mother was. For the sake of the others in the room, she elaborated. "She orchestrated a split between us, lying to each of us about the other." Caitlin shrugged. There was no point in mourning what could have been. She had her hands full working with what could still be. "We were young enough to believe her."

The judge nodded, fully understanding. Regina Cassidy was a very strong-willed woman, accustomed to getting her own way. He vaguely recalled a rumor that her daughter had been in love with a Native American, but that the romance hadn't worked out.

His eyes shifted toward Jake. "Since you saw fit to bring the boy in..." Harrison's voice trailed off as he beckoned Jake forward. "Come here, boy. Come stand by me." He turned his chair sideways, away from the desk, and waited.

Jake slid off his chair hesitantly. "My name's Jake," he said shyly.

"Jake." The judge nodded solemnly, as if this was news to him. He fixed the young face with a stern look. "Do you want to remain with your father, Jake?"

Wells was on his feet instantly. Though the proceedings were informal, he looked as if he was going to shout, "I object." "Your Honor, the boy's too young to know what he wants."

Harrison waved away the protest without sparing a look at Wells. "On the contrary, Mr. Wells, children know all too clearly what they want. Perhaps better than we do. Their vision of right and wrong isn't clouded yet. Or corrupted." He looked at Jake intently. If the boy lied, or had been coached, he would see. "Are you happy with your father?"

There was no hesitation, no looking over his shoulder for encouragement. "Yes."

The judge's hand remained on the boy's shoulder, commanding his full attention. "Does your father treat you well?" The small, dark head bobbed up and down in reply. "Does he hit you?"

"No." The denial popped up as if Jake wondered why the judge would even ask. "Does your dad hit you?"

For one of the very few times in her life, Caitlin saw the judge actually laugh. "Not recently." He released Jake and indicated that he was free to return to the shelter of his family.

Harrison turned his chair toward the desk again and addressed all parties concerned, beginning with Jake. "Well, you look well taken care of to me, Jake. I see no reason to change things."

Celia looked at the judge incredulously. "That's it? He looks well, so it's okay to leave him with his father?" Incensed, she rose in her chair. Her husband laid a restraining hand on her arm. After a moment she sank down again, sitting on the edge of her seat, a coil ready to spring.

The judge's gray eyes shifted to look at Celia. There was no warmth in them and only a pinch of understanding. "Mrs. Shephard, because you are his adoptive mother, the court grants you visitation rights. You may see your son one weekend a month and on alternate holidays. But I see no cause to disrupt what seems to be a happy, tranquil life. The boy shall go on living with his adoptive father and his stepmother."

This time Celia refused to be placated. She was on her feet before her husband or her lawyer could stop her. "You wouldn't be saying that if you two weren't friends.'' She jerked a thumb at Caitlin, her eyes filled with contempt.

Harrison seemed to rise several inches as he squared his shoulders.

"This is an informal hearing, Mrs. Shephard, so I shall overlook your tone. My friendship—albeit a distant one now—with Detective Redhawk's present wife has bearing in the case only insofar as I do not have to have the young woman's background examined prior to reaching my decision. Since I do know her, it allows me to dispense with that tedious aspect of this case and come to a more rapid conclusion.'' His mouth hardened. He had no patience with vacillations and Celia's had been particularly reprehensible to him. "You already gave up claim to the boy once.''

Celia's eyes widened and she looked at her lawyer helplessly. "Your Honor, Mrs. Shephard was going through a difficult time—''

"Difficult times can be gone through without shedding a child as if he were an unwanted skin. It does not seem to me to be in the boy's best interest to live with someone who is inclined to flitter in and out of his life, much like the tooth fairy, sporadically and on whim.''

He turned now toward Graham. His deportment didn't soften one iota. "From the research my clerks have done, Detective Redhawk seems to be an upstanding citizen, regardless of his financial holdings.'' He saw Wells opening his mouth and continued without pause. "If money is the issue here, his wife's estate more than makes up for that deficit. Jonathan Cassidy left his daughter quite well-off.''

Harrison folded his hands, coming to his conclusion. "So we are back to looking at things on an equal footing, as I originally stated.'' He raised a brow at Wells, challenging the man to say otherwise. "And given that, it is my decision that Jake Redhawk will continue to reside with his father.''

Wells was already beginning to gather his things. His face was red with anger he wasn't free to vent. "We'll appeal.''

Harrison had expected nothing less. "That is your God-given right in this wonderful country of ours.'' With no ceremony, he indicated the door. "Now, if you will all excuse me, I have another matter to tend to."

Celia spared a tearful look at Jake, undone by the way he hugged his father.

"This isn't over," she warned Graham as she stalked past him with her husband in attendance.

Zach felt like celebrating. If it wasn't that he had another case waiting for him on the fifth floor, he would have taken them all out for lunch.

He ushered Graham out, his hand clapped in friendship on the man's shoulder. "Round one's ours." Zach thought of what Graham had told him about Celia. "By the time the appeal comes up, with any luck—"

Graham nodded. "Her maternal mood will have passed." Although, knowing Celia, she might be stubborn enough to hold on, just to spite him.

Jake hopped from one foot to the other, excitement vibrating through his small body like a tuning fork. "Am I yours?"

Graham lifted the boy into his arms, holding him tightly as they walked into the corridor. "You've always been mine," he told him solemnly. He wanted the boy to remember that. "And no matter what would have happened here today, you would have always stayed mine."

"Listen, I've got to dash," Zach told them. "I'll be in touch should there be an appeal. Good luck to both of you!" he called enthusiastically over his shoulder as he hurried off.

Graham set Jake down on the bench that sat against the wall between two courtrooms. "Sit there for a minute, Jake. I have to talk to Caitlin."

Wondering what he wanted to say to her that he couldn't in front of Jake, she followed him to the side. He looked so out of his element, so unsettled. What was wrong?

There was an atrium in the middle of the floor. Graham looked at it absently, his hands shoved into his pockets. "I suppose I should say thanks."

It felt as if a wet rag had been dropped on her face. "Not if it has to be ripped off your tongue." He had her completely baffled. Graham looked like a man who had lost, not won. "What's the matter?"

The words were all tangled up inside him. "I just won my son. Why would anything be the matter?"

His tone was defensive. Angry. "I don't know, you tell me."

Graham blew out a breath, annoyed with her, with himself for feeling this way. But he couldn't help it. He'd been raised with a certain set of values, a certain view of the way things should be. Changing them challenged him as a man.

"All right, I didn't want to win because the judge bounced you on his knee."

Caitlin stared at him. "Excuse me? I didn't realize that there was a right and wrong way to win your son." Exasperation filtered through her voice. "What is your problem, Gray? So Harrison knew me and my father. So what? Whimsically, some other reason might have governed him, but it didn't. He's a tough old bird and he calls shots the way he sees them. Celia put up money, we put up money. Celia now has a place in the community. Well, so do we. And Jake wants to be with you. Voilà. He's yours. The main thing is that we won."

But it wasn't the main thing, she could see that. Somehow, her background was compromising his masculinity. Threatening him.

Damn it, why was he being so thickheaded?

"You married me in order to show the judge that your son had a mother, a balanced home life. You were using me as a tool. Why should it matter if I was more effective in one capacity than another?"

She wanted to shake him, to make him see things her way. "We're a team, Gray. Team members play the best they can and help each other any way they can. That's what *makes* them a team."

"Yeah, I know." He was being unreasonable and he knew it. But it still didn't change things. It still didn't make it any easier for him to accept the fact that Caitlin's background was probably the reason the judge had ruled in their favor.

He tried again. "Look, I know that maybe I'm being an ungrateful ass. Let me work this out for myself, all right?"

She supposed she couldn't ask for any more than that. "I'll give you all the time you want," she said softly, returning to Jake, "as long as you come up with the right answer."

Yeah, he thought, following her, but which answer was the right one?

Chapter 16

It wasn't often that he allowed himself to be preoccupied, but Graham was introspective this morning. He'd left the house with Jake's plea echoing in his ears, just as it did now.

"Can't you come to the game, Dad? Caitlin's coaching, so you don't have to do anything but watch us. Please, Dad?"

The plea tore at his heart. It felt as if in the past three weeks, since the judge's ruling, he'd slipped into second place within his own home, through his own actions. In trying to be fair to Caitlin, in attempting to rein in his own feelings for her and keep his distance, Graham had abdicated his position around Jake, as well.

It was Caitlin who now found ways to fill the void. Caitlin who took time off from work to take the boy to the movies, or to an amusement park. Or to pull the strings together for a friendly game of baseball. Caitlin who saw what was happening and didn't want the boy to suffer.

By attempting to keep as far away as possible from Caitlin, Graham found himself keeping the same distance from his son.

It was a no-win situation. He missed being with his son.

He missed being with her. He was going to have to find a way to resolve all this, and soon.

When Jake had begged him to attend this evening's game, Graham had promised that he would see what he could do. The look on Jake's face had told him that Jake didn't hold out much hope.

Caitlin had hurried through breakfast, wanting to squeeze a full day into five hours at the shop so that she could get to the field before the game began.

"Your dad'll be there if he can." She had looked at Graham then, silently begging him not to hurt Jake because of something that was going on between them.

The situation weighed heavily on his mind as he signed in on the board.

"Hey, Gray," Jeffers called from across the room. "There's someone here to see you." Ben pointed toward Graham's desk.

Now what? he wondered irritably as he made his way through the eternally crowded room.

The man who sat beside his desk was tall and athletic. He held himself as if he was ready to spring into action at a moment's notice. Relaxed tension, if there was such a thing.

Another cop, Graham thought, coming closer.

There was something vaguely familiar about the back of the man's head and the way he held himself....

A smile formed as recognition overtook Graham. Right about now, he thought, would be a good time to see an old friend again.

Graham came around to the front of his desk. His pleasure was genuine. His association with the other detective went back several years. A healthy respect for each other's capabilities had been born, as well as a strong, tacit friendship. Their paths hadn't crossed since then, but some people were destined to remain friends no matter how seldom they saw each other. It was that way with Kane Madigan.

"How's it going, Madigan?"

Detective Kane Madigan uncoiled his long, wiry body and

rose to his feet, taking the hand extended to him and wrapping strong, tanned fingers around it.

"Just fine." He flashed an easy grin. "Hear you're holding someone that we've been looking for."

Graham slung his jacket onto the back of his chair and sat down. His interest was piqued. "Oh?"

Kane nodded as he took out a Wanted poster and unfolded it for Graham. "A collar of yours."

A familiar face looked up at Graham from the poster. The man certainly was popular, he thought in disgust.

"Horace Taylor," he said without reading the name. Graham looked up at Kane, returning the poster. "What do you want him for?"

Folding the paper, Kane stretched out in his chair and tucked it away into the front pocket of his jeans. "He's wanted for questioning in a murder case. And suspected trafficking in black-market babies."

Graham understood. Recovering stolen babies was a personal crusade for Kane. It was while Graham had been assigned to a task force attempting to break a baby-kidnapping ring that he and Kane had met. Kane, heading the same sort of task force in Newport Beach, California, had been on the trail of a baby abducted from a local hospital. The baby had literally been taken from her mother's arms by a woman posing as a nurse. The child's mother had insisted on accompanying Kane every step of the way. Redhawk remembered being keenly impressed with her unwavering determination and her stamina.

That story, at least, had had a happy ending. There weren't many of those available.

Redhawk pointed a finger at the paper that had just disappeared into Kane's pocket. "Taylor's slime, all right."

The new black-market ring had been broken up. Taylor was just a loose end Kane wanted to tie up. And put behind bars where he could never touch another innocent life, never break another family's heart.

Kane looked at Graham with interest. "What's your collar?"

The question brought Caitlin back to mind. Who was he kidding? She'd never left his mind, not for more than a second or so.

"Murder one and attempted kidnapping." He wanted this man put away for a long time. Forever. "We have an eyewitness."

Since the man was behind bars here, Arizona had first dibs on Taylor. But Kane was taking a number. This was personal. No matter what other offenses Taylor had racked up in other states, Kane wanted Taylor to stand trial in California next. He laid his ankle across his leg. "Well, whenever you get through with him, we want him."

Graham thought of the term Taylor faced if convicted. "It won't be for a long time, that much I can promise you."

Kane heard the edge in the man's voice. Redhawk was a good cop, but there was something more going on here. "Sounds like you have a personal interest in him."

Showed that much, did it? Graham thought. Must be his white blood surfacing. The Navajo in him would never have allowed it to be so evident. "I do. He tried to kill my wife."

Kane's memory was jogged. He'd had a long conversation with Martinez before coming to pay his respects to Graham. The captain had mentioned Redhawk's recent marriage.

"Hey, that's right." Kane sat up, grinning. "I hear congratulations are in order."

Graham shrugged uneasily. After the past three weeks, he doubted very much if Caitlin would see it that way. "Yeah."

Kane studied Graham's face. Redhawk didn't seem like a man who felt that he had something to be congratulated about. Kane didn't believe in prying. But after living with Jennifer for so long, after being absorbed into her family, he no longer believed that each man was an island, either. Especially one who looked as if he was hurting. "Anything wrong?"

Graham shook his head. "Rough morning." He turned the conversation away from himself. "Whatever happened to that woman you were with? The one whose baby you located. Jennifer," he added, recalling.

Kane's grin returned, wider and brighter than the first time. "I married her."

Graham looked at him in surprise. Kane hadn't struck him as the marrying kind. He was more of a stoic, like himself.

He laughed. "You?"

"Yeah." Kane sat back in the chair, lacing his fingers behind his head. Sometimes it still caught him by surprise. Happiness. It was like an eternal Christmas package that he just kept opening and reopening. The delight never diminished.

"Best thing I ever did. Gave my life some kind of meaning, a focus." His voice strengthened. "I've got a family now." He dug into his pocket for his wallet. "Want to see a picture?"

Graham laughed again. Kane Madigan was the last person he would have expected to whip out a family photograph from his shirt pocket. If asked, Graham would have said that Kane was a great deal like him. Solemn, reserved. Dedicated to his job and little else. That description didn't seem to fit the contented man Graham saw sitting before him now.

Dutifully, Graham examined the photograph that Kane handed him. Kane was in the forefront with Jennifer. Two children shared their laps, one on each. A man and a woman, both vaguely resembling Jennifer, flanked them with their spouses and an entourage of small children.

"I see you used a wide-angle lens," Graham murmured. He handed the photograph back to Kane. "You look happy."

"I am." Kane returned the photograph to his wallet and then pocketed it. He hesitated a minute, knowing it wasn't any of his damn business. He could hear Jennifer whispering that it was. "Ask you a question?"

Graham shrugged. Kane probably wanted to know when they could begin extradition papers. "Shoot."

Kane wasn't good at choosing his words, so he shot straight from the hip. "Marriage not going well?"

Graham wasn't prepared for that sort of question. The look in his eyes darkened, warning Kane to back off. "It's going fine."

"Good." He was lying, Kane thought. They had more in

common than he thought. "Things take time, though, to work out. Niches to be found, that sort of thing," Kane drawled, sitting here as if he didn't have a dozen things he was supposed to be tending to on his desk back home. This seemed more important somehow, one former emotional cripple reaching out to another. "Me, I almost blew it. I walked away from her, you know." He slanted a look at Graham to see if he was getting through. "There she was, handing me my happiness on a platter, and I was running for the hills, thinking I didn't deserve it. Or her."

Kane looked off, seeing the past and not the men in the squad room. "Lucky for me I saw the light before it was too late. Otherwise, I'd still be living and sleeping police work and feeling empty on the inside." He looked directly at Graham. "Know the feeling?"

Talk about veiled lectures. Graham allowed himself a smile as he nodded. "Yeah, I know the feeling."

Kane was sure he did. He rose to his feet. "Well, I'd better be going. I've already talked to your captain about formally registering extradition papers for whenever Taylor's trial is over. Just thought I'd stop by and say hello."

Kane began to leave, then stopped and impulsively extended an invitation. Jennifer, he knew, would have been proud of him. "If you and your wife are ever in our neck of the woods, stop by. Jennifer would love to see you." Another piece of a memory returned. "Hey, are you still driving that pink Cadillac? What did you call it, again?"

"Esmerelda. Yeah, I'm still driving it."

The information pleased Kane. He nodded. "Nice to know some things never change."

No, Graham thought as he watched Kane leave the squad room, *some things never do.*

A small voice whispered in his soul that maybe some things should.

The late-afternoon sun was hotter than the interior of an oven, Caitlin thought. At least, it certainly seemed that way, sitting out here embroiled in a tense game of coach-pitch baseball with approximately twenty-four children who seemed to exert more energy than the heat warranted.

She felt wiped out and it was only the second inning. Of course, the second inning had lasted close to half an hour, what with stray balls, missed swings and two bats that had gone flying out of sweaty, slippery fingers.

Caitlin found herself wishing for a miracle. Maybe a sudden thunderstorm rising out of nowhere, ending the game and her misery.

The next moment she looked into a bouquet of dusty, hopeful faces waiting their turn at bat and felt guilty. What was a massive headache and borderline heatstroke in comparison to the unadulterated joy of a kid who had just managed to hit a triple?

She dug in, tabling her prayer for a miracle. She'd settle for the end of the second inning. The game was scheduled for five innings or an hour and a half, whichever came first. She had her suspicions which it would be.

Shading her eyes as another little boy from Jake's team went up to bat, Caitlin looked out across the field. She blinked, wondering if mirages occurred in populated areas. She thought she saw Gray crossing the dusty field, heading for their batting cage.

It couldn't be Gray. He was on night duty, where he'd been for the past three weeks.

"That's Dad!" Jake jumped up, abandoning his position in the lineup. The next moment he was hurrying to meet his father.

"Jake, you're batting second," she called after him. Caitlin held the batting helmet aloft.

He didn't hear her. Running, Jake reached Graham and wound himself around his father's frame as if he were part snake, part monkey. Exuberance and joy were written all over his face.

Jake hugged Graham so hard his own arms ached. "You came!"

For a moment Graham was overwhelmed by the display. Getting his own emotions under control, he nodded. "Yeah,

I came.'' He set the boy on the ground again. ''How're you doing?''

Grabbing Graham's hand, Jake dragged him the rest of the way to the batting cage. The pitcher, a man Graham vaguely recognized as the father of one of the neighborhood boys, waited until they reached the safety of the batting cage before he resumed pitching to the small boy at the makeshift plate.

''We're winning,'' Jake proudly announced in reply. He looked up at Caitlin for corroboration. ''Right?''

Caitlin nodded, her eyes on Jake rather than Graham. She was afraid Graham would see too much in her eyes if she looked at him. ''Right.''

''Keep it up,'' Graham told Jake. He looked at Caitlin as she slipped the batting helmet onto Jake's head. A crack of the bat echoed, followed by an encouraging shout. Belatedly, the batter began to run for first as another child went scurrying to retrieve the ground ball. ''Hi.''

''Hi.'' She scooted Jake toward the plate. ''You're up next.'' Watching Jake take his position at bat, Caitlin glanced at Graham. ''I thought you were on night duty.''

The reception was chilly. He couldn't blame her. He'd been making a concentrated effort to keep distance between them. There was no reason to be surprised that he had succeeded.

''I asked Martinez to reassign me.'' She looked at him sharply. ''I told him I thought I was missing too much.''

He was talking about Jake, she insisted silently, afraid to let herself think that he meant what she desperately wanted him to mean. She nodded, just barely acknowledging his words.

He was getting what he deserved. What he had wanted. So why did it feel so bad? Maybe it was because, for a glimmer of a moment, Kane had shown him what his own life might be like if he was willing to risk the attempt.

Maybe it was already too late. He'd pushed her away with both hands, thwarting any and all of her attempts to bridge the gap, to form a bond. He had told himself that he had been doing it for her. Maybe it was himself he was doing it for. Because the thought of happiness, elusive happiness, scared the hell out of him. It scared him because he was afraid that if he had it, if he got used to it, he would lose it. The way he'd once thought he'd lost her.

But not having her while she was so close was even worse.

"Choke up on the bat, Jake," she called. When Jake looked at her in confusion, she moved behind the boy and showed him what she meant. She moved his hands farther up on the shank of the bat. "Like this. Okay?"

"Okay."

Caitlin stepped back, out of range.

She was making his son happy, Graham thought. What was he doing, throwing all this away without even trying to make it work? "You're pretty good at this."

Still watching Jake, Caitlin shoved her hands into the back pockets of her white shorts. Shorts that adhered to her like a second skin, Graham thought, watching the inviting shift of her hips as she tensed, watching Jake.

"A month ago I didn't know the first thing about playing baseball," she answered. She glanced at Graham over her shoulder. "I just did a lot of reading up on the game, called around, talked to the people who organized coach-pitch teams. You know, the usual."

Graham looked at Caitlin. She'd done a hell of a lot more than that. She had gone ahead and organized baseball teams when Jake had expressed an interest in playing the game. Getting a list of his friend's phone numbers from Jake, Caitlin had got on the telephone and called all the parents, telling them about her idea. She had invited everyone to join in, or at least to send their children. Games were to be played, strictly for fun, two evenings a week and early on Saturdays. It caught on within a day and now was a regular event.

Jake's team was comprised of seven boys and five girls, all eager for their turn at making the ball fly. Pitchers and base coaches were parents. Caitlin, the only woman involved, had been made honorary head coach.

Or head mascot, Graham thought, looking at her. She had that cuddly look. Or was that just his longing, slipping out again?

God, but he missed her.

He had only himself to blame.

She could feel Graham's eyes on her and it was unnerving her, turning her to liquid faster than the sun.

"Are you staying?" If he was, she was going to direct him to sit with the rest of the parents who had come straggling in to watch their offspring play.

"Yeah, I'm staying." He looked at the handful of fathers on the field. He might as well make himself useful. Standing here beside her inhaling her fragrance was making him a little crazy. "Where do you want me?"

She spared him a glance before looking back at Jake. The count on the boy was three and two. He had five swings in all coming to him. She hoped that at least one would make contact with the ball.

"Loaded question," she couldn't help answering. "Are you serious?"

"Don't I look serious?" He spread his hands before him. *You look wonderful.* Caitlin cleared her throat. "Okay, for starters, how about coaching first base? All you have to do is tell them when they should run. One of the volunteer fathers didn't show. I've got kids ready to fly at every pitch."

Graham was already heading for first. "Gotcha, Coach."

Wary, burned more than once, Caitlin was afraid to let out the warm feeling that was trying to seep through. He was here only because of Jake, nothing more.

The final score was thirty-one to twenty-six in favor of Jake's team. They took the win the way only seven-and eight-year-olds could. Ecstatically.

Walking on air, the children left the field of victory with their parents, leaving Caitlin and company to collect the assorted bats, helmets and balls and pack them away until the next game.

"Who does all this belong to?" Graham asked as he helped her gather everything together.

"Us. I decided to supply the essentials for the team. It was either that, or no game." She glanced at Jake as he brought her the last of the stray balls. "Jake would have been too disappointed if that had happened."

She really cared about the boy, Graham thought. Perhaps almost as much as he did. He hadn't really thought about that. About Caitlin becoming entangled in Jake's life, as well. It added another dimension to the equation.

Jake threw the remainder of the balls into the large black sack, his eyes shining.

"Did ya see, Dad? Did ya see? I hit a home run!" It was only the third time he'd announced it to them.

Delight soared through him at the sheer joy on Jake's face. Graham laughed as he impulsively hooked an arm around his neck and hugged his son to him.

"Yeah, I saw."

"That was for you, Dad." Jake said importantly, as if he was capable of directing his hits. "'Cause you came." Jake danced from foot to foot, unable to contain himself. "Are you gonna come to the next game?"

Caitlin tugged on the drawstrings of the large sack, waiting for an answer.

He wondered if she felt as if he was barging in. "I'd like that."

"Good. I could use a batboy," Caitlin said. She dropped the drawstrings and the sack listed, the top drooping to the ground. "Why don't you carry that to the car?"

Graham hefted the sack, balancing it on his shoulder. He looked down at Jake walking beside him. "Gives orders well, doesn't she?"

"You bet." His eyes shifted to Caitlin as they reached the cars. "Can we go out for hamburgers and fries, Cait? Can we? 'Cause this is such a special time?"

"You mean because you won?" she asked as she unlocked the trunk.

"No, 'cause we're all together." He backed up as his father deposited the sack into the trunk.

Caitlin's eyes met Graham's. This was his call. "Ask your dad, Jake."

Jake's head seemed to swivel as he turned toward his father. "Can we?"

Graham almost said no, that they had better head home, and then he remembered Kane's photograph. "Sure. Why not? I've got the night free."

What was he up to? Caitlin wondered. There had to be some catch, some reason he was doing this other than the simple one of just wanting their company.

Leaning inside her car, she dropped her purse between the two front seats. "This *is* a special occasion."

He'd been conspicuously absent from her life for the past three weeks. It seemed that, once the court had granted him custody, he didn't need her anymore. He was just biding his time until they could call it quits. That was what she had verbally agreed to, but living through it was killing her.

She knew Graham had purposely volunteered for night duty just to have an excuse to stay away from her. She had accepted it stoically, for the time being resigning herself to living within the confines of this marriage of convenience she had agreed to. Things didn't change overnight, and neither would Gray.

In the meantime she did have some pride, she told herself. She couldn't keep throwing herself at a man who was refusing to catch her.

"Jake, why don't you ride with your dad and I'll follow behind you."

Jake happily began to comply, then turned at the last minute and looked at Caitlin. "You don't mind?"

It touched her that he cared. "I don't mind. Go."

Caitlin and Jake staked out a booth, then waited until Gray returned with their order. The fast-food restaurant, a favorite with the under-twelve set, was filled with parents taking their kids out for the evening. She waved to Gray when she saw him looking blankly around.

Seeing her, he picked his way carefully to their table. Graham set the tray down. Sodas and cheeseburgers shared space with fries that insisted on spilling out and melding with everything.

She watched him, waiting until he'd had a few bites of his burger before asking. "So why did you suddenly show up on the field today?"

She was asking him things he wasn't ready to say yet. "I already told you. I was switched from night duty."

Caitlin munched her fry slowly, her eyes on his. "Switched?" she questioned innocently.

She was on to him and playing cat and mouse. Maybe she'd earned it, he thought. He had been pretty distant with her. "Yeah, I thought it was time I got back to leading a normal life."

Caitlin smiled into her tall paper cup. Attempting to maintain a sober expression, she looked up at him. "Any special reason for this sudden epiphany?"

Jake looked from his father to Caitlin and back again. Something was going on, but he didn't understand what. "What's a piffy?"

"Epiphany," she repeated. "That's when the Holy People give you a vision." Caitlin raised her eyes to Graham. "Or do I have my traditions confused?"

He was smiling at her, she thought, actually smiling. Maybe that miracle she'd asked for had gotten rechanneled somehow. Instead of a thunderstorm magically appearing, she'd gotten Graham, smiling at her. Given the situation lately, that was a miracle in its own right.

"Yeah, but that's okay." He took one of her fries on purpose. "You're a paleface. You're entitled."

She grinned. Resting her elbow on the table, she leaned her face on her upturned hand. "You still haven't answered my question. *What* made you change your mind?"

"I saw an old friend today. Someone I would have sworn was more like me than I was."

Her eyes were dancing as she regarded him. "Wooden, huh?"

Laughing, he pushed a fry into her mouth. "He seemed pretty happy."

"So you arrested him," she teased, winking at Jake, who giggled.

He liked the sight of that, his son sharing a moment with Caitlin. Something warm rose within him, unclenching the tightened fist that seemed to be so much a part of his makeup.

Graham shook his head. "I asked him why."

Suddenly it seemed very important for her to know what he had learned from this friend whom he had thought was so much like him. This friend who was happy.

"And?"

"He has a wife and family now. It seems to suit him pretty well." There was a crash from the front counter as a man dropped his tray. Graham leaned over the table and raised his voice to be heard. "He said he'd fought against it, thinking that it wasn't right for him." Graham realized that he was shouting. And that he was very, very close to Caitlin. "Turns out it was."

Her smile bloomed slowly across her lips and flowered in her eyes. Nurtured by her soul. "I'd like to meet this man."

He nodded. He'd like that. He'd like Caitlin to meet Kane and Jennifer. And for them to meet her. "Maybe we'll take a vacation down there someday. He lives in Southern California."

Jake, engrossed in finding different ways of bending his fries and then eating them, suddenly came to life. "Disneyland?" His eyes grew wide.

Graham maintained a straight face. "Yeah, I think he mentioned he lives near there."

"When can we go?" Jake was almost on his feet, ready to dash out.

He couldn't hold his smile in check any longer. Graham ruffled Jake's hair. "Maybe soon."

Jake looked from Graham to Caitlin. Of the two, Caitlin was the softer one. "Tomorrow?"

"Not that soon." Graham laughed just as his beeper went off, sending out a staccato beat.

Jake looked accusingly at the beeper clipped to his father's belt. "You're making noise, Dad."

Graham shut it off. He didn't want to be interrupted. Not tonight. "Yeah, I know."

Jake hated his father's beeper. It always took him away just when they were having fun. "Don't they know you're at a 'portant victory dinner?"

Graham rose to his feet. "I'll tell them. Right now, I've got to find a phone."

"There's one in front of the doughnut shop two doors down," Caitlin told him.

Jake applied himself to the fries as his father walked out. He made short work of them and then snuck a couple from his father's container.

Caitlin raised a brow. "He counts them, you know," she said solemnly.

The fry he was about to pop into his mouth stopped in mid-descent. "He does?"

"Yup." She nodded, suppressing a smile. "If there's one missing, he'll know."

Jake looked as if he wasn't sure if he believed her, but he didn't want to take the chance.

Coming to the rescue, she switched some of her remaining fries into Graham's container. "Here, we'll slip him some of mine. He'll think they're his."

Satisfied, Jake grinned. "Thanks, Cait. You're the best."

Well, she'd won over at least one Redhawk. "Tell that to your father."

Small brows drew together over bright brown eyes. "Doesn't he know?"

She shook her head as she toyed with her straw. The soda was already beginning to taste flat. "I don't think so."

"He's smart," Jake insisted. "He knows." He snuggled up to her. "I like you, Cait. You're fun."

"Glad you think so." She looked up and saw Graham walking toward them. The solemn expression was back on his face. It didn't look promising. "Uh-oh."

Jake turned to see what she was talking about.

"Is it time for Cinderella to leave the ball?" Caitlin asked as Graham joined them.

"Ball's been canceled." He didn't bother sitting down. Instead, he beckoned them to their feet. "C'mon, let's go."

Jake rose, befuddled. "Home?"

"Home," Graham said firmly.

There was no arguing with his tone. Caitlin gathered her things together. "Now you're beginning to sound like me." She slid out of the booth. "Why's the ball being canceled?"

He took hold of her arm as he ushered Jake in front of him. "That was Jeffers on the phone." This wasn't easy for him to tell her. It was even more difficult for him to live with. "They were transferring Taylor to a maximum-security prison. It's not usual procedure before an arraignment, but there are more charges cropping up that look as if they belong to him."

Caitlin felt her stomach knotting. "What happened?"

"He escaped." Graham saw the color drain from her face. "C'mon, I want to get you two home. Now."

Chapter 17

Caitlin shook her head in answer to Graham's request as she strode into the living room. Lily, sensing that trouble was brewing, gently urged her grandson to go play in the backyard. Jake went, complaining that he wanted to ride his bike with his friends instead. His manner indicated that he felt pent-up.

That made two of them, Caitlin thought. And she was determined to do something about it. She was going to work whether Graham liked it or not. Caitlin picked up her purse from the coffee table. Ready, she faced Graham, prepared to go to the mat over this one.

"I won't stay home any longer, Gray. I feel like my whole life's been put on hold for the last week, waiting for someone to apprehend Taylor. I can't go on like this."

It had been a week since they'd heard that Taylor had escaped. A whole week of remaining at home while she let Kerry handle everything at the shop. A whole week of staying put while Graham left every morning, chasing down clues. And then returned home at night, frustrated and solemn, too tired to even talk.

She had dropped her bombshell on him as he was on his way out to the precinct. Graham looked at her incredulously. "You can't go out."

Ignoring him, Caitlin opened her purse and checked for her car keys.

Damn, he didn't have time for this. "Caitlin, be reasonable."

She whirled around on her heel, ready to do battle. He might not see things her way, but that was too damn bad. She had had it.

"I *am* being reasonable. For all we know, this guy's back in California or Nevada. Or maybe even somewhere else. He moves around," she reminded Graham, quoting what he had told her about the criminal. "Why should he stay here, with a murder and kidnapping rap hanging over him?" Exasperated, feeling like a prisoner, she threw up her hands. "Maybe he's gone out to scout new territory. All I know is that the store is mine and it's not fair to make Kerry and Eva do all the work." She shifted impatiently from foot to foot as she eyed the front door.

She made it sound as if she were being kept at home because of a whim instead of for her own safety. Why couldn't she just stay put for a few more days? There was an intense manhunt on for Taylor. A few more days might make the difference in his capture and then she would be free to do what she wanted.

As would he. There was a great deal he wanted to discuss with her, a great deal he'd had to put off because of Taylor's escape.

Graham blocked her path. "What do you mean, fair? You're not exactly on a vacation."

"No—I'd enjoy a vacation." She fixed him with a hard look as she pushed him out of her way. "Look, you didn't want to marry me originally because you didn't want to place your mother and son in jeopardy. Well, having me here does just that."

"Which is exactly why there's a squad car posted right outside, and one patrolling the area." He wasn't about to take foolish chances, the way she obviously wanted to. "I thought you just said you thought he was gone."

He would catch that. She frowned. If she didn't get out, she was going to scream. "People with cabin fever tend to contradict themselves. Now, I'm going to work." She crossed to the front door. "You can follow me or not, that's your choice, but unless you're placing me under arrest, I am leaving."

Right after the game last week, Caitlin had been certain that they were on the brink of a breakthrough. Something was finally clicking into place between them.

But then Jeffers had called and everything had fallen apart. News of Taylor's escape had brought everything to a sudden, screeching halt. They were right back to where they had been after the hearing in Harrison's chambers. Square one. Graham was out being a detective again, and she was home without him. Except now she didn't even have her work to help hold her sanity intact.

But she couldn't stand doing nothing anymore. There was just so long she could put up with watching summer reruns. If she watched one more game show, she was going to throw something at the television set.

"So, if you're not going to arrest me," she challenged, "I've got a shop to run and a baseball game to coach later."

God, was she out of her mind? Wasn't almost getting dragged away once by that maniac enough for her? "You can't go to the game."

She drew herself up on her toes, still over half a foot shy of him. "What's he going to do? Sneak up on me and shoot me in the middle of a crowd? How's he going to get to me? There's no cover."

For two cents he'd throttle her. "Ever hear of a rifle with telescopic sights? Snipers can hit a gnat from half a mile away."

"Well, I'm not a gnat and this guy likes to be inches away, watching the life ooze out of his victims." She'd heard the pleasure in Taylor's voice when he had shot the man in the alley. It gave her nightmares. "I don't think he'd settle for long-distance thrills."

Graham looked at her. Either she was very brave or very stupid. At this moment he wasn't about to bet which. "You know that and you're still willing to go out?"

"Gray, I can't live my life hiding. Not from anyone. Not *for* anyone." She looked at him pointedly. If he would just say something to her that she could cling to, it might help. But he was so distant, almost obsessed with his work. She was beginning to think she had fooled herself into thinking that there was still something there between them. "Now get out of my way. Some of us have places to be."

She had guts, he'd give her that. His mouth softened. "You've turned a damn sight more stubborn than when I last knew you."

She shrugged, her back to him as she slipped the strap of her purse on her shoulder. "Yeah, well, maybe I grew up."

Yes, he thought, she had. A great deal. The fire in her eyes made her even more incredibly appealing than she already was. He thought of what he longed to do; what duty and the need for a clear head, the need to be alert, prevented him from doing. But this was no time to even think about that. He had to place his personal feelings and desires on hold until Taylor was caught. Until she was safe.

"Caitlin—"

Something in his voice made her look at him. He wasn't about to continue lecturing her. There was something else there. "Yes?"

He let it drop. For now. There was no use starting something that couldn't go anywhere at the moment. He promised himself that tonight they'd talk. Meanwhile, he could sympathize with the way she felt, cooped up, even if the policeman in him knew it was for the best.

"Let me make a few phone calls to arrange things and then I'll take you in."

That wasn't what he had been planning to say to her, she thought. She told herself to stop hoping. The mountain never came to Muhammad. And Muhammad, it seemed, couldn't make a dent in the damn mountain.

She nodded. "Wise choice."

He blew out a short breath. Yeah, right. This definitely went against his better judgment. "Not the way I see it."

The squad car remained in front of the house. Another one was waiting, parked in front of the lingerie shop, when they arrived. Graham told Caitlin that the patrolman's name was Reynolds.

"How long does this protective custody go on?" she wanted to know as he pulled into the parking lot in front of her store.

"Until I say it stops."

She frowned. Were so many patrolmen necessary? "Why aren't you enough? You were before." She got out of the car.

"I wasn't personally involved before. You're my wife now."

In name only. Caitlin raised a brow as she approached the front door.

"Might do you good to remember that." She tossed the remark over her shoulder before she pushed the door open.

He watched her walk in, her hips swaying ever so slightly. *I remember, Cait. All too well.*

The bell went off, announcing her arrival. She was quickly the center of an impromptu reunion of one. Kerry threw her arms around her and held on tight.

"I've never been so happy to see anyone in my whole life." Kerry looked toward Graham. "You, too, Detective."

He murmured something unintelligible in response. Caitlin laughed. The two customers in the store looked on in mild surprise. Caitlin scanned the store. "Where's Eva?"

"Out sick. It's only me today." She lowered her voice. "I'm so sick of lingerie I may burn all mine."

"Shh." Amusement shone in Caitlin's eyes. "Don't let anyone hear you say that. It's bad for business."

Kerry was definitely drooping. She had never been able to hold a candle to Caitlin where energy was concerned. "I'm beginning to think *I'm* bad for business. We haven't been doing that well the last couple of days.''

''Don't worry, the cavalry is here,'' Caitlin assured her. She glanced over her shoulder at Graham. ''Sorry about that.''

She was in her element here, Graham thought. She already looked more alive than she had for the past week. He suddenly realized that Caitlin thrived on work. He'd never known that about her. It was something he could identify with. ''As long as the cavalry is you, there's nothing to be sorry about.''

Caitlin thought that, in an odd sort of way, he'd given her a compliment. She smiled. Maybe they hadn't lost all that headway they'd made last week after all.

She went to work immediately. Having done little of anything for almost a week, she was dying to feel useful. She redid displays, went over the past week's accounts and waited on customers.

She seemed to be everywhere, Graham thought. And she loved it.

''You look tired,'' Caitlin told Kerry. Kerry had barely nibbled on her lunch, muttering something about coming down with Eva's cold. ''Why don't you take the rest of the afternoon off?''

Kerry felt guilty as she looked around the store. In only three hours Caitlin had done far more than she had in a week. She chewed on her lower lip. ''Are you sure you won't mind?''

''I'm sure. It feels great being able to do something again.'' Caitlin glanced around the store. It did feel wonderful, being useful. ''I just might repaper the walls this afternoon,'' she teased.

Reprieved, Kerry nodded absently. She went digging for her purse under the counter and saw the small, off-white envelope she had shoved there for safekeeping. She pulled it out, chagrined that she had forgotten it until now.

''By the way, this came for you.'' She held out the delicate-looking envelope to Caitlin. ''It was delivered to the store Monday.''

The white linen envelope was perfumed. Caitlin recognized the scent instantly. She didn't have to bother looking at the handwriting to know who it was from. There was no return address.

"Mother," she murmured.

Graham and Kerry exchanged looks. "Maybe you'd better—" Graham began, his hand outstretched.

Caitlin shook her head. She didn't need to be protected from this. "Nothing she can say will bother me." She'd finally gone past that. Oh, she would still have welcomed a reconciliation, but she didn't believe in fairy tales and she knew her mother. This letter was *not* about a reconciliation.

Looking as unaffected as if she had just glanced at a flyer offering precise detailing for her car, Caitlin scanned the letter quickly, then crumpled it up. She tossed it into the wastepaper basket beneath the counter.

"There, that's where it belonged in the first place."

He understood her apparent desire to keep the contents of the letter to herself. After all, he didn't like talking about his problems. But he knew Caitlin was different. She needed to share, to talk. And more than that, she needed someone to listen.

"What did your mother have to say?" he asked.

Caitlin shrugged carelessly. "Mother's having a fit, but that's her prerogative." Her eyes met Graham's. She saw his silent question. "Someone told her that I'd married you. According to her letter, if I don't divorce you instantly, I will be disowned and disinherited."

There was a great deal of money at stake. He couldn't allow her to lose that because of him. "Maybe you'd better explain to her…"

Kerry looked from one to the other, curious. "Explain what?"

Caitlin wasn't about to tell Kerry that she and Graham had entered into a bargain rather than a marriage of substance.

"That she's an idiot." Caitlin's eyes warned Graham not to say anything further. "And that if she hadn't disowned me,

I would have probably gotten around to disowning her. She just saved me the trouble.''

Caitlin turned to face her friend. Her mouth softened. ''Now, go home, Kerry. I have a business to run and it's not helping me any if you're standing around wilting on the premises.'' She nodded toward the closest display, a handful of slinky peignoirs overlapping one another. ''These garments are supposed to be exciting, not sleep inducing.''

Kerry nodded, glad for the reprieve. ''Don't have to tell me twice.'' She hugged Caitlin extra hard and then left, passing a customer on her way in.

Her mother's letter weighed heavily on his mind. Graham placed his hand on her arm. ''Caitlin, we have to talk....''

She didn't like the look in his eyes and she had a feeling that she'd like what he had to say even less. ''Not right now, Detective. I have a customer.'' She crossed to the woman quickly, pasting on her lips a cheerful smile she didn't feel.

Over the next hour there was a steady stream of customers coming into the store. She managed to keep none of them waiting.

Graham sat back, feeling a measure of pride as he watched her, as well as the prick of guilt. He knew Caitlin's mother meant what she said and Caitlin was too proud, too stubborn to give in.

If he really loved her, he'd let her out of this marriage before her mother carried out her threat. But that was the trouble; he did love her and he had finally stopped playing games with himself. It had happened exactly the way he had feared. She'd gotten so entrenched in his life that now he didn't want her to leave him for any reason. Ever.

He fingered the box in his jacket pocket, the one that had been there for the past three days, and struggled with his thoughts. His heart was doing battle and holding its own with his mind.

Maybe he should just—

The telephone rang. Caitlin had her hands full with three customers. He rose and crossed to the back room. ''I'll get it.''

Looking in his direction, Caitlin nodded, grateful for the help. She put the call completely out of her mind until he emerged again. When she looked, she saw that he was shaken.

She excused herself for a moment and left the three women to their selections. "What is it?"

The hospital clerk's voice was still echoing in his head. Following Caitlin's example, Jake had rebelled and gone out to ride his bicycle. He'd been hit by a motorist as he darted out between two parked cars. The paramedics on the scene had found the identification card Jake carried with him and had given it to the ER clerk. He had called the precinct, which had directed the call to the shop.

His mouth was grim. "That was someone from the hospital emergency room. There's been an accident." He saw her grow pale. "Jake's been hurt."

It felt as if all the air had suddenly been extracted from her lungs. How? When? Her mind whirled as she struggled to get hold of it. "Wait, I'll get my—"

He shook his head. Damn it, how many times had he told the boy to be careful? "No, you stay here. I'll tell Reynolds to stay close. He'll keep an eye on things until I get back." Graham was already at the door.

He was cutting her off again, she thought. Drawing that same damn line in the sand, separating her from the others, just as he had that first day in his house.

She remained where she was. "Call me as soon as you find out anything."

He barely nodded as he hurried out.

Caitlin had tried to keep her mind on her work, but it was impossible. She kept wondering how Jake was doing. As if to make things worse, the steady influx of customers into her store had abated. A lull set in, the way it usually did right after two. This time it grated on her nerves. If there had been wallpaper handy, she just *might* have repapered the store the way she had jokingly said to Kerry.

She glanced at her watch. Why hadn't he called her? He'd

been gone almost thirty minutes. That was enough time to reach the hospital and find Jake. Why—?

The bell rang softly. Caitlin looked up from the display she had rearranged three times. But it was only the patrolman Graham had left to guard her. The tall policeman closed the door behind him with great care.

"Too hot for you out there, Reynolds?" she asked pleasantly.

He nodded shyly, the brim of his cap dipping down into his eyes.

"Have you heard anything from Detective Redhawk yet?" She didn't expect he had, but it didn't hurt to ask.

"No."

Well, he certainly wasn't talkative. Must be a requirement to join the force, she mused. "I've got some cold soda in the storeroom in the back," she offered. "I'll get you one."

Without waiting for the man to comment, Caitlin turned toward the storeroom. The area seemed particularly airless to her when she opened the door. The cool air that wafted out of the refrigerator was more than welcome. She lingered a moment, though the soda was right at her fingertips.

She'd just closed the refrigerator when her hand was grabbed from behind. Her heart jumped, beating wildly as she tried to turn around. She'd been held like this before. In the fast-food restaurant.

But how? There was a patrolman just a few feet away. The patrolman. She twisted, trying to get a look at the man's face.

"Taylor?" she whispered.

"Yeah." The voice, low, raspy, was filled with pleasure, with glee. It made her flesh creep. "It's me. And now, bitch, you're about to pay for all the inconvenience that you've caused me."

Graham knew he was operating on maximum overload. He felt pushed to the wall and exhausted. Otherwise, he would have been thinking more clearly and telephoned the hospital back after he'd received the call. He wouldn't have driven halfway there before the thought occurred to him.

Fear drove icy spears through Graham. A bright red light was winking madly on the roof of his car as a siren screamed, demanding the cars before him scatter. He'd already called for backup.

No one had called him from the hospital. His son wasn't lying there mangled. He was still home with his grandmother. A call patched through for him by dispatch had given Graham that information. In addition to another piece that should have made him happy. Celia had dropped the suit. But right now the only thing that would've made him happy was having Caitlin at his side.

He'd driven off, leaving her life in the hands of one inexperienced patrolman. Damn, where had his mind been? Reynolds was far too new at this to be a match for someone clever enough to learn the ins and outs of someone's life in order to get at his target.

To get at Caitlin.

The psychological profile on Taylor had labeled him as obsessive with borderline traits of insanity.

And Caitlin was his target.

Graham floored the gas pedal, shooting through lights with almost reckless abandon until he reached Caitlin's store. He was the first one there.

His car fishtailed as he brought it to a stop beside the patrol car. One glance showed him it was empty. It could very well be that Reynolds had just gone inside to stay closer to Caitlin, but something just didn't feel right.

Now his instincts kicked in. Where the hell had they been when the phone call had come? He knew the answer. Buried beneath a father's concern. Just as Taylor had known they would be.

If he so much as touched her—

"Caitlin!" Graham yelled out her name as he ran into the store. It was eerily deserted. Damn it, where was she? "Caitlin!"

He'd come back too soon. Taylor had counted on at least five more minutes. Enraged, he pulled the woman's arm all the way up, twisting it behind her.

Caitlin bit her lower lip to stifle the whimper. It felt as if her arm was snapping off.

"Any other way out of here?" Taylor demanded.

She moved her head from side to side, almost dizzy from the pain. She fought to remain conscious. "Just the front."

"Then we'll take the front."

There was death in his voice. Caitlin's heart froze. "Please don't hurt him. I'll do anything you say, just don't hurt him."

Taylor laughed harshly. "There's nothing you *can* do. What's one more corpse, more or less?" Taylor jerked her arm harder. "And for what you put me through, bitch, you're going to watch him die first."

Still holding her arm behind her back, he began to push Caitlin out of the storeroom just as Graham reached the rear of the shop. His gun was drawn, ready.

Taylor turned to face him, his weapon aimed at Caitlin's temple. She could feel his smile pulling his lips away from a perfect row of teeth. Ghoulish.

"Let her go," Graham ordered, his eyes steely, flat. "Let her go and take me."

"Touching," Taylor snorted. "Very touching, but I'm not letting anyone go. Now, you put that down or she dies right here, right now."

He was crazy, Caitlin thought. He was actually enjoying this. Her mind scrambled for a way out before it was too late. And then he drew the muzzle of the gun away from her temple, aiming it at Graham.

He was going to kill Gray, just as he'd said.

With a scream that was equal parts terror and rage, Caitlin rammed her free elbow into his stomach, throwing herself against Taylor. The shot went wild as they both fell to the floor.

"Move, Caitlin!"

She didn't know if she rolled away before or after Graham yelled the order. She just rolled.

On the floor, Taylor fired again. The gun dropped from his fingers as the bullet from Graham's weapon found its mark.

Just like that, it was over.

Without realizing it, Caitlin had squeezed her eyes shut. She felt Graham's hand reach for hers. Very slowly he helped her to her feet.

He was shaking inside as he held her to him. He didn't want to think what could have happened.

"That was a damn stupid thing to do," he murmured. She was safe. He had her and she was safe. "He could have killed you."

"Funny," she whispered, her words disappearing into his chest, "the same thought occurred to me about you."

"Detective?" Someone called from the other room.

"In here," he responded. His arms tightened around Caitlin.

She sagged against him. Now that it was over, her knees didn't feel very strong. "A little late, aren't they?"

The next moment the storeroom was filled with uniformed policemen. Graham released her. "Better late than never."

"Detective?" the tallest policeman began. "We found Reynolds in the alley. Taylor must've found a way to lure him away." He pressed his lips together. "He's dead."

Graham nodded. He'd expected as much. Taylor had only one mode of operation. Elimination. "Get this scum out of my sight."

Graham looked down at Caitlin, then tucked his arm around her shoulders. "You need air."

She merely nodded and let him lead her out. "Jake—?"

"He's fine. It was all a ruse."

It was over, she thought, looking around as evening flirted with the streets of Phoenix. It was finally all over.

"Are you all right?" He stroked her hair.

"Fair to middling." She sighed, attempting to get hold of herself.

She might be, but he wasn't. It was hard to forget what might have happened to her. He held her by the shoulders, looking down at her face.

"You scared the hell out of me. When I thought—" Emotion choked off his voice.

Oh, no, he wasn't just going to leave her hanging like this. "When you thought what, Gray? When you thought—?"

He backtracked, his hand cupping her cheek. "When I realized that he had set me up, that he was going to—damn it, Caitlin, don't ever scare me like that again."

She smiled sadly. "I'll try not to."

He must have been crazy to try to push her away. "He won't bother you anymore."

"No, he won't. We can go back to life as usual." Whatever that meant. She looked down at her hand. "Oh, damn."

He didn't see anything to warrant her distress. She wasn't hurt. "What?"

"My ring. It's gone." She held up her hand. Her ring finger was naked. "I must have lost it when I was struggling with him in the storeroom."

The thought of losing it, the outward symbol of what she had hoped to build, was unbearable. She turned, ready to tear the storeroom apart until she found it. Graham's hand on her shoulder held her back. She tried to shrug him off. "Gray, I have to find it."

"Is this it?" He held up a ring.

She took it from him, confused. "This isn't mine." It was a small band encrusted with tiny diamonds. She raised her eyes to his. "It's gorgeous."

He took the ring from her and slipped it on her finger. "It's yours."

She was afraid to lead with her heart again. "But—"

He cut through her protest. "All you have to do is accept what comes with it."

A smile began to form in her eyes. "Which is?"

"Me."

Caitlin wrapped her arms around his neck. "You idiot, I accepted you a long time ago." She searched his face, attempting to understand. "What made you change your mind?"

"I didn't change my mind so much as lose the will to fight against myself anymore." He smiled into her eyes, her beautiful turquoise eyes. "I tried to picture life without you again and couldn't. I can't give you up, Caitlin, not of my own free will.'' His expression was rueful. ''I don't have any where you're concerned.''

''Nice to know.'' Her body leaned into his, drawn by the heat, sealed by the need. It was finally really going to be all right. The relief was enormous. As was the anticipation. ''This marriage of convenience hasn't been convenient for me at all.''

He whispered a kiss along her temple. ''For me, either.''

She liked the sound of that. ''Want to do something about it?''

He saw the mischief that entered her eyes. Kane was right, sometimes you didn't know how damn lucky you really were. ''Such as?''

''Closing up the store and going to a hotel for the night?'' She thought of her wedding night and her smile widened. ''Someplace tacky.''

''Sounds good to me.'' She started for the door, but he held her back. Now was the time to share the rest of his news. ''When I called my mother to verify Jake's whereabouts, she told me that my lawyer called.''

''Oh?'' She braced herself.

''Celia's husband convinced her it would be better for everyone concerned if they went ahead and adopted a baby on their own. She finally agreed. So there's really no need for a marriage of convenience anymore.''

''Good.'' She allowed herself to enjoy the momentary confusion that rose to his eyes. ''Now the real thing can start.'' She turned toward the shop again. ''Just let me go in and get one of the negligees before I lock up.''

But he caught her hand before she could enter. ''Nothing against your merchandise, Caitlin, but you're not going to need it.''

A smile played on her lips. ''Then what am I going to wear, Gray?''

His eyes were already making love to her. "Me, Caitlin. Me."

She could feel the glow building within her. "Sounds like a perfect fit to me."

*   *   *   *   *

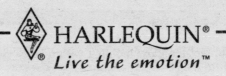

HARLEQUIN®
Live the emotion™

Heart, Home & Happiness

HARLEQUIN®
Blaze

Red-hot reads.

HHH Harlequin® Historical
Historical Romantic Adventure!

HARLEQUIN®

HARLEQUIN ROMANCE®

From the Heart, For the Heart

HARLEQUIN®
INTRIGUE
Breathtaking Romantic Suspense

Medical Romance™...
love is just a heartbeat away

HARLEQUIN®
Presents
Seduction and Passion Guaranteed!

HARLEQUIN®
Super Romance

Exciting, Emotional, Unexpected

www.eHarlequin.com

HDIR08

HARLEQUIN ROMANCE®

The rush of falling in love,

Cosmopolitan,
international settings,

Believable, feel-good stories
about today's women

The compelling thrill
of romantic excitement

It could happen to you!

EXPERIENCE
HARLEQUIN ROMANCE!

Available wherever Harlequin Books are sold.

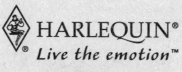

HARLEQUIN®
Live the emotion™

www.eHarlequin.com

HROMDIR04

HARLEQUIN®
INTRIGUE®

BREATHTAKING ROMANTIC SUSPENSE

Shared dangers and passions lead to electrifying
romance and heart-stopping suspense!

Every month, you'll meet six new heroes
who are guaranteed to make your spine tingle
and your pulse pound. With them you'll enter
into the exciting world of Harlequin Intrigue—
where your life is on the line
and so is your heart!

THAT'S INTRIGUE—
ROMANTIC SUSPENSE
AT ITS BEST!

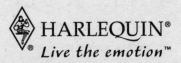

HARLEQUIN®
Live the emotion™

www.eHarlequin.com   INTDIR06

HARLEQUIN®
Super Romance®

…there's more to the story!

Superromance.
A *big* satisfying read about unforgettable
characters. Each month we offer *six* very different
stories that range from family drama to adventure
and mystery, from highly emotional stories to
romantic comedies—and much more! Stories
about people you'll believe in and care about.
Stories too compelling to put down….

Our authors are among today's *best* romance
writers. You'll find familiar names and talented
newcomers. Many of them are award winners—
and you'll see why!

If you want the biggest and best
in romance fiction, you'll get it
from Superromance!

Exciting, Emotional, Unexpected…

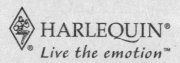

HARLEQUIN®
Live the emotion™

www.eHarlequin.com   HSDIR06

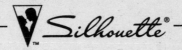

SPECIAL EDITION™

Emotional, compelling stories that capture the intensity of living, loving and creating a family in today's world.

Desire

Modern, passionate reads that are powerful and provocative.

nocturne

Dramatic and sensual tales of paranormal romance.

Romances that are sparked by danger and fueled by passion.

Visit Silhouette Books at www.eHarlequin.com

SDIR07

∀ *Silhouette®*

SPECIAL EDITION™

Emotional, compelling stories that capture the intensity of living, loving and creating a family in today's world.

Special Edition features bestselling authors such as Susan Mallery, Sherryl Woods, Christine Rimmer, Joan Elliott Pickart— and many more!

For a romantic, complex and emotional read, choose Silhouette Special Edition.

Visit Silhouette Books at www.eHarlequin.com   SSEGEN06

SAFE HAVEN

PRESENTING THE SAFE HAVEN™ COLLECTION!

Risk everything...
for a love that matters!

YES! Please send me the exciting *Safe Haven*™ collection. This 50-book collection will begin with 2 FREE BOOKS and 2 FREE GIFTS in my very first shipment—and more valuable free gifts will follow! My books will arrive in 8 monthly shipments until I have the entire 50-book *Safe Haven* collection. I will receive two free books in each shipment and I will pay just $4.49 U.S./ $5.69 CDN. for each of the other four books in each shipment, along with $1.99 for shipping and handling*. If I decide to keep the entire collection, I'll have paid for only 32 books because 18 books are free. I understand that accepting the 2 free books and gifts places me under no obligation to buy anything. I can always return a shipment and cancel at any time. My free books and gifts are mine to keep no matter what I decide.

265 HDK 9415 465 HDK 9425

Name	(PLEASE PRINT)	
Address		Apt. #
City	State/Prov.	Zip/Postal Code

Signature (if under 18, a parent or guardian must sign)

Mail to the **Harlequin Reader Service:**
IN U.S.A.: P.O. Box 1867, Buffalo, NY 14240-1867
IN CANADA: P.O. Box 609, Fort Erie, Ontario L2A 5X3

Want to try two free books from another line?
Call 1-800-873-8635 or visit www.morefreebooks.com.

* Terms and prices subject to change without notice. Prices do not include applicable taxes. N.Y. residents add applicable sales tax. Canadian residents will be charged applicable provincial taxes and GST. This offer is limited to one order per household. All orders subject to approval. Credit or debit balances in a customer's account(s) may be offset by any other outstanding balance owed by or to the customer. Please allow 4–6 weeks for delivery. Offer available while quantities last.

Your Privacy: Harlequin is committed to protecting your privacy. Our privacy policy is available online at www.eHarlequin.com or upon request from the Reader Service. From time to time we make our lists of customers available to reputable third parties who may have a product or service of interest to you. If you would prefer we not share your name and address, please check here. ☐

SHBPA08